Longitudinal Space-Charge Waves

MODERN ELECTRICAL
STUDIES

A Series Edited by

Professor G. D. SIMS

Head of Department of Electronics
University of Southampton

Longitudinal
Space-Charge Waves

R. E. TROTMAN

M.Sc., C. Eng., A.M.I.E.E., A. Inst. P.
Senior Research Fellow in Bio-Engineering,
St. Mary's Hospital Medical School, London

CHAPMAN AND HALL LTD
11 NEW FETTER LANE, LONDON, EC4

First published 1966
© *Robert Edward Trotman* 1966
Printed in the Netherlands by
Nederlandse Boekdruk Inrichting N.V.

Contents

Preface

There are a number of books on physical electronics and many of them introduce space-charge waves. However, to the author's knowledge, no single volume yet published gives a complete and detailed treatment of the longitudinal space-charge-wave theory. Whilst it is appreciated that there has recently been a shift of emphasis from devices whose operation depends on space-charge waves to those whose operation is more concerned with the solid state, it was felt that there is a demand for a monograph giving a concise but thorough exposition of the evolution of the theory.

This is such a monograph and its contents may be summarized as follows. A brief review of the early history of the subject and information on some fundamental properties of waves and electron beams introduce the work. This is followed by a detailed discussion of the theory of propagation of longitudinal space-charge waves on both mono-velocity and multi-velocity electron beams moving in magnetic focusing fields. Theoretical mechanisms for producing increasing space-charge waves on single electron beams are considered and some experimental amplifiers are described and discussed. The interactions between two electron beams are examined in considerable detail and some practical devices that utilize the increasing space-charge wave obtained in such reactions are described and discussed. The power flow associated with space-charge waves is also considered.

It is hoped that this monograph will be of great value to final year undergraduate and post-graduate students of electrical engineering and physics. Those concerned with teaching them may well find collected here all the information on space-charge waves they require.

The author wishes to make it perfectly clear that a considerable amount of material has been taken direct from published papers and from company reports, and readers will doubtless realize that such material could not have been used without the permission of the Editors of journals and/or individual authors. It is sincerely believed that adequate acknowledgements of the sources of information, and of the original workers involved, have been made in the text. Should there be any omissions, it is quite unintentional. The author humbly apologizes for any such omissions and expresses his gratitude to all who so readily gave permission to use the material concerned and to those who supplied the private communications.

It will be appreciated that a volume of this nature is not the unaided work of the author. It is impossible to name all those who have contributed to its production and it would be invidious to select a few. Nevertheless, one would be ungracious not to acknowledge the assistance of Dr J. E. Houldin, of Chelsea College of Science and Technology, who made many valuable suggestions and who devoted a great deal of time to checking the manuscript. His enthusiasm and ready willingness to help and advise have been invaluable. To the numerous other helpers and advisers – my grateful thanks.

R. E. T.

CHAPTER 1

Introduction

1.1 BRIEF HISTORICAL REVIEW

A great stride in the microwave tube field began with the work of Clavier [1], who gave the first explanation of how amplitude modulated or bunched current could arise as a result of the action of an r.f. field on an initially uniform electron beam. He dealt with a system that had no drift-space, but finite transit time in the interaction space, and it was Heil and Heil [2] who produced the first genuine velocity-modulation tube, although this did not have a cavity resonator. Soon after this, several papers were published. One described the rhumbatron [Hansen, 3], one described the klystron [Varian and Varian, 4] and another the velocity-modulation tube [Hahn and Metcalf, 5]. All these devices have a drift-space, a space in which the beam is not operated on by any external fields, and a device at each end for modulating or de-modulating the beam. In principle, the operation is as follows. An a.c. voltage is applied to one modulator, and this is arranged so that electrons passing through in one half-cycle are accelerated and those passing in the other half-cycle are retarded. The beam is then said to be velocity-modulated, although some space-charge modulation also exists. In the drift-space, the faster electrons catch up with those slowed down in the preceding half-cycle, so that there is an increase in electron density at one part of the beam (a bunch is formed) and there is a decrease in electron density at another part of the beam. Where there is a bunch, the potential of the beam is more negative, therefore the electrons tend to move towards a less crowded position (the electrons tend to de-bunch). When the bunch passes the second modulating/demodulating device it induces an electric current into the electrodes. If there is an impedance (resistance) between them there is an opposing electric field which extracts energy from the beam. Thus, all the electrons in the bunch are slowed down.

The above description is the basis of Webster's [6] 'ballistic' theory of velocity modulation, given in his classical paper on cathode ray de-bunching published in 1939. The optimum length of the drift-space (or tube) is discussed in Sect. 2.2.2.1.

Despite this great stride, the velocity-modulation tubes have limitations. It has already been suggested that as soon as a bunch is formed, the electrons tend to de-bunch due to the repulsion forces between the individual electrons. These are the space-charge forces and they reduce the change in velocity due to the velocity-modulation process and hence the efficiency of the velocity-modulation mechanism. These effects cannot be adequately explained by the Webster theory and it is clear, therefore, that a different theory is required to describe more fully the operation of these tubes.

A clue to the crux of the matter was, in fact, given by Webster [6] in his paper. He wrote:

'... any one electron on its way through the bunching space is surrounded by *waves of space-charge*, in which the change of amplitude from one wave to the next is so slight that the problem of calculating the de-bunching forces ...'

and this is the first time to the author's knowledge that space-charge waves were referred to in any way. Also in 1939, Hahn [7] published the first attempt to investigate the possibility of axial waves existing in a moving electron beam, but the war suddenly created a great demand for klystrons, both amplifiers and oscillators, and the effort devoted to the development of such tubes was greatly increased. Most of the theoretical studies made at that time were based on Webster's theory and Hahn's ideas received little attention. This was probably due to a few things, the most important being that Webster's theory had been generally accepted as giving a satisfactory description of the operation of the oscillators and power amplifiers then in vogue (requiring a large-signal theory), and Hahn's theory is extremely complicated as is seen in Chapter 2. This, coupled with the simplicity of Webster's theory may well explain the trend which, with hindsight, one can say was to the detriment of the development of microwave devices.

It was not until 1947 when Kompfner [8] first described the travelling-wave tube, that more attention was paid to the possibility that space-charge waves propagate on moving electron beams as predicted by Hahn. The original explanation of the operation of the travelling-wave tube was given by Pierce [9]. This was essentially a ballistic theory, but as the currents in the electron beam were increased, so the Pierce theory had to be modified by introducing space-charge factors. The space-charge-wave theory then began to receive more attention than hitherto, particularly as the operation of all the devices in use could not be explained entirely by the Webster and Pierce theories.

Before proceeding to discuss space-charge-wave theory in detail some important fundamental facts are introduced, as a knowledge of them is assumed throughout.

1.2 FUNDAMENTAL DATA

1.2.1. Conventions

It is assumed that the electron charge is $-e$ and the number density n for electrons is given by $\rho_0 = -ne$. The coordinate systems used are shown

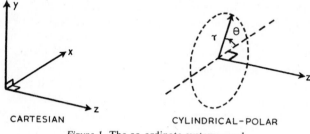

CARTESIAN   CYLINDRICAL-POLAR

Figure 1. The co-ordinate systems used

in Figure 1 and the positive direction of velocity is in the positive z direction. We use $J_0 = \rho_0 u_0$ and therefore the convection current is in the negative z direction, since, for electrons ρ_0 is negative.

1.2.2. The electron beam

A very important property of electron beams is the natural plasma oscillation frequency, invariably shown by the symbol ω_p. Tonks and Langmuir [10] first showed that if one had a collection of ions or electrons in equilibrium and one ion or electron is displaced from its equilibrium position, then it will oscillate about its equilibrium position. The natural oscillation frequency of electrons was shown to be (neglecting collisions)

$$\omega_\mathrm{p} = \sqrt{(-e\rho_0/m\varepsilon_0)} \ .$$

The oscillation is simple harmonic. The negative sign applies because, for the electron, the space-charge is negative and the charge on the electron is also negative, and so ω_p^2 is positive. This often causes confusion in the literature and the negative sign is often omitted. It is simpler to use the number density

$$n = -\rho_0/e$$

therefore $$\omega_\mathrm{p} = \sqrt{(ne^2/m\varepsilon_0)}$$

and there can be no ambiguity. This is rarely used, however, and one has to be careful not to get the signs wrong in some of the algebra. A glance at much of the literature will quickly verify this statement. Whilst our chief concern is with electrons, exactly the same applies to ions; but since they are heavier, collisions cannot be neglected and the formula is slightly different. For our purpose it is assumed that for electrons $\omega_\mathrm{p} \ll \omega$, the frequency of the r.f. signals applied to the beam. Since ω_p (for electrons) is of the order of 500 Mc/s the work applies solely to the microwave range of frequencies.

Another important property that we are concerned with is the total derivative of the velocity of an electron with respect to time. This often occurs since the equations of motion are used, particularly the equation

$$m(dv/dt) = -eE \ .$$

If the velocity is a function of z and t only

$$\frac{dv}{dt} = \frac{\partial v}{\partial t} + \frac{\partial v}{\partial z}\frac{\partial z}{\partial t} \ . \qquad 1.1$$

Now dv/dt applies to a particular electron; it moves along with a particular electron, but $(\partial v/\partial t)_{z=\text{const}}$ applies to a particular point in space and hence to different electrons.

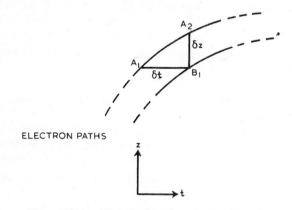

ELECTRON PATHS

Figure 2. The total derivative of an electron in motion

Consider an electron at point A_1 of the distance time curve (Figure 2). The velocity of the electron is given by the slope of the curve at that point. If by the time the electron has moved a distance δz, to point A_2, a time δt has elapsed and the velocity has changed by an amount δv, then

$$\text{Lim} \, (\delta v/\delta t)_{\delta t \to 0} = dv/dt \, .$$

Assume now that instead of moving from point A_1 to point A_2 we move to point B_1, keeping z constant. In this case, the velocity has changed by $(\partial v/\partial t)_{z=\text{const}} \delta t$ but it will be observed that we have moved to another electron. Consequently, the new velocity no longer applies to the first electron; we have to add a velocity component $(\partial v/\partial z)\delta z$ to obtain the true velocity of the first electron. Note we assume a continuum of charge in the electron beam and do not concern ourselves with the quanta themselves. Hence dv/dt really applies to a particular volume element of the moving beam. Further discussion of the total derivative is left until Section 1.2.3.

1.2.3. Some properties of waves

Throughout this monograph it is assumed that any wave motion at a single real frequency ω varies as $\exp\left[j(\omega t - \gamma z)\right]$. By $\exp(j\omega t)$ we always mean the real part, but γ is given by

$$j\gamma = \alpha + j\beta$$

where $\alpha \equiv$ attenuation constant,

$\beta \equiv$ phase constant and

$\gamma \equiv$ propagation constant.

Thus the wave varies as $\exp\left[j(\omega t - \beta z)\right]\exp(-\alpha z)$. Note that z is the direction of propagation.

Interest centres around the propagation constant γ and whether or not it is complex or has only a real part (in this case $\gamma = \beta$). If it is complex, then α is either positive or negative, which means that the wave decreases or increases in space. Further discussion of this point occurs in Chapter 3. (Care should be taken when reading the literature. Often one finds $\exp(j\omega t - \gamma z)$ being used and in this case γ is sometimes assumed to be given by $\gamma = \alpha + j\beta$.)

If now we assume that motion can take place only in the z direction, we can put $\partial/\partial t = j\omega$ and $\partial/\partial z = -j\gamma$ and therefore Eqn 1.1 becomes

$$dv/dt = (j\omega - u_0 j\gamma)v$$

u_0 being the d.c. velocity of the electrons.

Therefore $\qquad\qquad dv/dt = j(\omega - \gamma u_0)v$

or, for any other variable that varies as $\exp\left[j(\omega t - \gamma z)\right]$

$$d/dt = j(\omega - \gamma u_0) \qquad\qquad 1.2$$

or $\qquad\qquad d/dt = j\omega_b$

where $\qquad\qquad \omega_b = (\omega - \gamma u_0)\ .$

ω_b is the Doppler shifted frequency; the frequency seen by the electrons, which is the same as the frequency seen by an observer moving at velocity u_0, the velocity of the electrons.

Finally, it is necessary to discuss the 'velocity' of the wave. In fact there are two velocities that a wave may possess and these will be treated separately.

The *phase velocity* is the velocity at which the wave train appears to be moving. The wave carries no information (no energy) until it is switched or modulated. By definition, the phase velocity u_p is given by

$$u_p = \frac{\text{distance travelled by the wave}}{\text{time of travel}}$$

and it is simply shown that $u_p = \omega/\beta$. If γ is real $u_p = \omega/\gamma$.

The *group velocity* is the velocity at which energy is transported. If the carrier wave is modulated, a modulation envelope will beat with the carrier. If we have two waves, travelling at different velocities and at different frequencies, the envelope travels at a velocity equal to $\partial\omega/\partial\beta$ and this is the group velocity u_g

therefore $$u_g = \partial\omega/\partial\beta \ .$$

A more detailed discussion of phase and group velocity is given in Hutter [11].

CHAPTER 2

Propagation of Space-Charge Waves on Mono-Velocity Electron Beams

2.1. GENERAL REMARKS

In June 1939, the first attempt to investigate the possibilities of axial waves existing in a moving electron beam was published by Hahn [7]. The analysis was limited to the 'ideal' case in which the electron beam is of uniform density throughout, and described space-charge waves with axial symmetry only.

This paper indicated for the first time, that the operation of the velocity-modulation tube could be explained in terms of waves propagating along the tube. In August 1939, Ramo [12] extended the analysis by considering waves with velocity components in all directions. In December of that year, Ramo [13] repeated some of the earlier work but used retarded potentials for the magnetically focussed beam and in addition, discussed some of the factors that affect the practical design of so called velocity-modulation tubes. Hahn [14] published an extension of his original work in November 1939, considering the quantity of any waves generated by an r.f. voltage across a gap. The subject of energy in space-charge waves was also introduced.

It is evident, therefore, that within a period of six months in 1939 the foundations of space-charge-wave theory were laid. The ramifications become evident in the development of the theory through to modern times.

We commence by considering in some detail the Hahn-Ramo theory of longitudinal space-charge waves in infinite or very high longitudinal magnetic fields.

2.2 PROPAGATION IN INFINITE OR VERY HIGH LONGITUDINAL MAGNETIC FIELDS

2.2.1. Assumptions

Unless specifically stated at any particular juncture, the following assumptions are made throughout the whole of Section 2.2:

(a) A.C. values are very small compared to d.c. values. This enables us to neglect products of a.c. quantities, thus linearizing the equations.

(b) The radius of the electron beam is held constant by an infinite or very high longitudinal d.c. magnetic field, parallel to the direction of motion of the electrons.

(c) The axial d.c. velocity of the electrons is constant.

(d) The radial velocity of electrons is zero.

(e) The d.c. space-charge density of the beam is constant.

(f) The same number of positive ions as electrons are present, moving with the same axial velocity as the electrons. This produces a steady magnetic field to balance out the tangential magnetic field of the electrons, and also ensures that the equilibrium space-charge electric field is zero.

(g) The positive ions are assumed to have infinite mass so that they have no a.c. motion.

(h) The velocity of the electrons is very much less than the velocity of light. This enables us to neglect the a.c. values of magnetic field [Hutter, 11].

This is a formidable list of assumptions and they are discussed later. It is, however, very important to appreciate that without making assumption (a), the equations would become extremely complicated and the physical significance of the solutions be lost in a mass of mathematical detail. One could say the same for assumption (h). To summarize, a one dimensional, small-signal, low velocity analysis of a neutralized beam is made.

10   LONGITUDINAL SPACE-CHARGE WAVES

2.2.2. Beams of finite cross-section drifting in a coaxial conducting cylinder

2.2.2.1. *The Hahn analysis*

Hahn solved Maxwell's equations (see Appendix 1) by the method of substitution, considering the a.c. and the d.c. parts separately, for the general case. He then found solutions for the case of motion along the axis.

The assumed variations of E_r etc. for inside the beam are of the form

$$E_r = \hat{E}_r J_1 (T_0 r)\, e^{j(\omega t - \gamma z)}$$

(where J_n is a Bessel function of the 1st kind and nth order) and the equations required are

(A1.1) $$\nabla \times \mathbf{E} = -\frac{\partial \mathbf{B}}{\partial t}$$

(A1.2) $$\nabla \times \mathbf{H} = \frac{\partial \mathbf{D}}{\partial t} + \mathbf{J}$$

(A1.9) $$\nabla . \mathbf{B} = 0 \qquad\qquad 2.1$$

(A1.10) $$\nabla . \mathbf{D} = \rho$$

and the Lorentz equation $\quad \mathbf{F} = e\left[\mathbf{E} + (\mathbf{u} \times \mathbf{B})\right].$

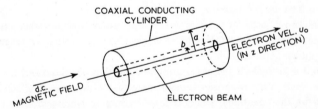

Figure 3. Illustration of the system used in the Hahn analysis

The basic procedures of the analysis are briefly described below (Figure 3 shows the symbols used in the analysis).

(1) Eqn A1.10 the θ component of Eqn A1.1 (A1.4), the r and z components of Eqn A1.2 (A1.6 and A1.8) and the z component of the

Lorentz equation involve E_r, E_z, H_θ, v_r, v_z, and ρ. These equations are solved for five of these quantities in terms of the sixth, namely E_z. J_r and J_z are obtained from $\rho_0 v_r$ and $(\rho_0 v_z + \rho u_0)$ respectively. Also, if r is the radial displacement of an electron whose undistorted radius is r_0, then

$$r = r_0 + r_1 J_1(T_0 r)\, e^{j(\omega t - \gamma z)}.$$

These quantities are all involved in the 'E_0' type of wave.

(2) The r and z components of Eqn A1.1 (A1.3 and A1.5) and the θ component of Eqn A1.2 (A1.7) involve the quantities E_θ, H_r, H_z and v_θ. These equations are solved for three of these quantities in terms of the fourth, namely E_θ. J_θ is obtained from $\rho_0 v_\theta$. These quantities are all involved in the 'H_0' type of wave.

(3) The r and θ components of the Lorentz equation are used to obtain a relationship between E_z and E_θ, the amplitudes of the 'E_0' wave and the 'H_0' wave respectively. This is called the coupling equation and is found to be

$$E_\theta = \frac{-\gamma}{T_0}\, \frac{\omega \omega_L}{c^2} \left\{ \frac{T_0^2 + g\left(\gamma^2 - \dfrac{\omega^2}{c^2}\right)}{\left[T_0^2 + \gamma^2 - \dfrac{\omega^2}{c^2} + \dfrac{\omega_p^2}{c^2}\right]\left[\gamma^2 - \dfrac{\omega^2}{c^2} + \dfrac{\omega \omega_b}{c^2}\right]} \right\} E_z.$$

(4) The r and θ components of the Lorentz equation are also used to obtain a relationship between T_0 and γ. [This requires a knowledge of E_z and the solutions of E_r etc. (see 1 above) enable us to calculate all the amplitudes thus giving the relationship between T_0 and γ]. The resulting equation is called the determinantal equation and is found to be

$$\left[T_0^2 + \gamma^2 - \frac{\omega^2}{c^2} + \frac{\omega_p^2}{c^2}\right] = \frac{\omega_c^2}{g\omega_p^2}\left[T_0^2 + \gamma^2 - \frac{\omega^2}{c^2}\right]\left[T_0^2 + g\left(\gamma^2 - \frac{\omega^2}{c^2}\right)\right].$$

If T_0 is imaginary, it is convenient to replace T_0 by $j\tau_0$ where τ_0 is real and substitute $I_1(\tau_0 r)$ for $J_1(T_0 r)$ and $I_0(\tau_0 r)$ for $J_0(T_0 r)$. The results then hold for τ_0 if $j\tau_0$ is substituted for T_0 and $-\tau_0^2$ for T_0^2.

The determinantal equation is a biquadratic in T_0, so in general there are two values of T_0^2 for each value of γ^2. At the boundary, these values are indistinguishable except that they produce different ratios of tangential electric to magnetic field.

The assumed wave solutions for outside the beam are of the form

$$E_z = \left[F_z J_0(T_1 r) + G_z Y_0(T_1 r) \right] e^{j(\omega t - \gamma z)}.$$

These are similar to those assumed for inside the beam, except that Bessel functions of the second kind $Y_n(\gamma r)$ are included [$Y_0(\gamma r) \to -\infty$ as $r \to 0$ and therefore cannot be used in problems in which the origin is included] and the function T_1 is used in place of the function T_0. Hahn also inserts the effective dielectric constant k which enables one to take glass effects into account. In this case $\rho = 0$ and Maxwell's equations have to be suitably modified. The determinantal equation is found to be

$$T_1^2 + \gamma^2 - \frac{\omega^2}{c^2} k^2 = 0.$$

As in the previous part of the analysis, if T_1 is imaginary, we substitute $j\tau_1$ for T_1 and $-\tau_1^2$ for T_1^2. It should be pointed out here that Hahn did not specifically name either T_0 or T_1, they merely appeared in his assumed solutions.

The analysis is completed by applying boundary conditions. We assume that there is a perfectly conducting outer boundary at a radius bR_1, with a vacuum between the beam and this conductor.

The two conditions used are:

(1) At the outer conducting boundary the tangential electric intensities must be zero.

Therefore $\qquad\qquad E_z = E_\theta = 0.$

(2) At the edge of the beam E_θ, E_z, B_θ and B_z, as calculated from the equations derived from both inside and outside the beam, are equated.

There are two values for T_0 for a given value of γ, so that the equation for inside the beam has to take both these values into account. There is only one value of T_1.

Thus for inside the beam:

$$E_z = \left[E_{z1} J_0(T_{01} b) + E_{z2} J_0(T_{02} b) \right] e^{j(\omega t - \gamma z)}$$

at a radius $r = b$. We note that the equilibrium beam radius b is assumed instead of the radius r_b given by

$$r_b = b + r_1 J_1(T_0 b) e^{j(\omega t - \gamma z)}$$

(this is assumption (b) – the radius of the electron beam is held constant).

The solutions obtained after applying the boundary conditions, together with the determinantal equations for inside and outside the beam, provide three equations for γ, T_0 and T_1, so that the values of γ may be obtained.

If γ is real then the solutions are unattenuated waves. Hahn called these 'true' waves. If, however, γ has an imaginary part, some gain or attenuation is present. To have a wave the real part of γ must also be present. True waves may exist in an infinite tube, but those with gain or attenuation may not, because the attenuation constants have finite values only near a discontinuity.

Tonks called waves with attenuation 'local' waves since they are confined to a small region. It is as well to emphasize here that we are almost exclusively concerned with steady state conditions.

The general equations obtained from the above analysis are complicated, and at the time Hahn produced his theory they had not been used for the design of tubes. In order to simplify the solutions, we consider the special case of $\omega_c = \infty$. As $\omega_c = (e/m) B_{z0}$, the cyclotron frequency, this is the case of $B_{z0} = \infty$, the case to which the assumptions limit the analysis.

The beam determinantal equation

$$\left[T_0^2 + \gamma^2 - \frac{\omega^2}{c^2} + \frac{\omega_p^2}{c^2} \right] = \frac{\omega_c^2}{g \omega_p^2} \left[T_0^2 + \gamma^2 - \frac{\omega^2}{c^2} \right] \left[T_0^2 + g \left(\gamma^2 - \frac{\omega^2}{c^2} \right) \right]$$

gives two values of T_0^2 in this case.

$$T_{01}^2 = - \left(\gamma^2 - \frac{\omega^2}{c^2} \right) \qquad\qquad 2.2$$

and

$$T_{02}^2 = -g \left(\gamma^2 - \frac{\omega^2}{c^2} \right) \qquad\qquad 2.3$$

where $\quad g = \left(1 - \dfrac{\omega_p^2}{\omega_b^2}\right)$

ω_p = plasma frequency and

ω_b = Doppler shifted frequency $[= \omega - \gamma u_0]$.

Comparing Eqn 2.2 with the determinantal equation for outside the beam

$$\left[T_1^2 + \gamma^2 - \frac{\omega^2}{c^2} k^2 \right] = 0$$

and remembering that $k = 1$ (assuming that no glass is present) we see that

$$T_{01} = T_1$$

and that all quantities except E_θ, H_r and H_z are zero. But E_θ, H_r and H_z are all involved in the H_0 wave. Since no electron movements are permissible in the r and θ directions the H_0 wave cannot cause such movements. Indeed, the H_0 wave does not exist. We shall not consider this case any further.

If we now take Eqn 2.3 and substitute into the relationships for the quantities involved in the E_0 wave we obtain values of E_r, etc.

If $(\omega/c) \ll \gamma$:

T_1^2 is negative, and we therefore put $\tau_1^2 = -T_1^2$,

$$\tau_1^2 = \left(\gamma^2 - \frac{\omega^2}{c^2}\right).$$

Therefore $\quad\quad\quad T_{02}^2 = -g\tau_1^2$.

Combining the solutions obtained after applying boundary conditions and the coupling equation gives

$$-\frac{\sqrt{(-g)}J_1[\sqrt{(-g)}\tau_1 b]}{J_0[\sqrt{(-g)}\tau_1 b]} = \frac{I_1(\tau_1 b) - \dfrac{G_z}{F_z}\bigg|_1 K_1(\tau_1 b)}{I_0(\tau_1 b) + \dfrac{G_z}{F_z}\bigg|_1 K_0(\tau_1 b)} \qquad 2.4$$

(where $\dfrac{G_z}{F_z}\bigg|_1$ is the value of this ratio inside the beam) having substituted

$-g\tau_1^2$ for T_{02}^2, $I_1(\tau_1 b)$ and $I_0(\tau_1 b)$ for $J_1(T_1 b)$ and $J_0(T_1 b)$, and $K_0(\tau_1 b)$ and $-K_1(\tau_1 b)$ for $Y_0(T_1 b)$ and $Y_1(T_1 b)$.

Assuming T_{02} is real (i.e. g is negative; since τ_1 is real) Eqn 2.4 is a relationship between $\sqrt{(-g)}$ and $\tau_1 b$. If we assume values of $\tau_1 b$ we can find the corresponding values of $\sqrt{(-g)}$.

Putting
$$a' = \tau_1 b \sqrt{(1-g)} \qquad 2.5$$

and substituting for $\sqrt{(-g)}$ in Eqn 2.4 produces an equation for a' in terms of $\tau_1 b$.

It should be noted that only constants concerning the geometrical configuration of the boundary are involved in this equation.

Now
$$\tau_1 b = \pm b \sqrt{(\gamma^2 - \omega^2/c^2)}$$

and
$$g = (1 - \omega_p^2/\omega_b^2)$$

and since
$$a' = \tau_1 b \sqrt{(1-g)}$$

$$a' = \pm \tau_1 b (\omega_p/\omega_b)$$

$$a' = \pm \frac{\tau_1 b \omega_p}{(\omega - \gamma u_0)} \, . \qquad 2.6$$

Since
$$\gamma = \pm \left(\tau_1^2 + \frac{\omega^2}{c^2} \right)^{\frac{1}{2}}$$

we have
$$a' = \pm \frac{\tau_1 b \omega_p}{\omega \mp u_0 \sqrt{(\tau_1^2 + \omega^2/c^2)}} \, . \qquad 2.7$$

Thus for a given set of values of ω_p, ω and u_0 Eqn 2.7 can be plotted as a' versus $\tau_1 b$.

If this equation is plotted on the same axes as Eqn 2.5 (combined with (2.4)), the points of intersection of the two curves are the values a' and $\tau_1 b$ corresponding to all values of ω_p, ω and u_0 as well as the assumed boundary conditions.

Curves for a typical case are given in Figure 4, and there are two points of intersection.

(In solving Eqn 2.4 one finds that there is an infinite number of values of $\sqrt{(-g)}$ for every value of $\tau_1 b$. This in effect gives the values of γ

for an infinite number of waves, but we shall consider the first order waves only. The effect of higher order waves is dealt with in Appendix 6.)

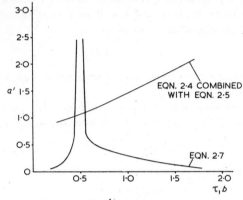

Figure 4. Solution of the modified coupling equation (Eqn 2.4) in the Hahn analysis

Finally, substitute $\tau_1^2 = (\gamma^2 - \omega^2/c^2)$ into Eqn 2.6

$$a' = \pm \frac{b\omega_p}{(\omega - \gamma u_0)} \sqrt{\left(\gamma^2 - \frac{\omega^2}{c^2}\right)}$$

therefore

$$\left(\frac{\omega}{u_0} - \gamma\right)^2 = \left(\frac{b^2 \omega_p^2}{a'^2 u_0^2}\right)\left(\gamma^2 - \frac{\omega^2}{c^2}\right), \qquad 2.8$$

which gives, assuming a' to be constant,

$$\gamma_{1,2} = \frac{\omega}{u_0 \left(1 - \dfrac{b^2 \omega_p^2}{a'^2 u_0^2}\right)} \left\{ 1 \pm \frac{b\omega_p}{a' u_0} \sqrt{\left[1 - \frac{u_0^2}{c^2}\left(1 - \frac{b^2 \omega_p^2}{a'^2 u_0^2}\right) \right]} \right\}. \qquad 2.9$$

Now if $\gamma = \omega/u_0$ the phase velocity of the wave (ω/β) is equal to the velocity of the electron beam u_0 (since γ is real, $\gamma = \beta$).

If a' is assumed constant and if $(\omega_p b/a' u_0) \ll 1$, then $\gamma_{1,2} = \dfrac{\omega}{u_0}(1 \pm \delta)$ where δ is very small. Thus we have two waves, one with phase velocity slightly lower than the beam velocity (γ_1), and the other with phase velocity slightly greater than the beam velocity (γ_2). Since, in both cases, γ is real these waves are unattenuated. If the two waves exist simultaneously, they form a wave of average velocity and with a variable amplitude.

The variation in the direction of motion of the beam is

$$A'\,e^{-j\gamma_1 z} + B'\,e^{-j\gamma_2 z}$$

and if $A' = B'$ (the two waves are equally excited) the variation is

$$2A'\cos\left(\frac{\gamma_1-\gamma_2}{2}\right)z\,.\,\cos\left(\frac{\gamma_1+\gamma_2}{2}\right)z\,.$$

But

$$\left(\frac{\gamma_1+\gamma_2}{2}\right) = \frac{\omega}{u_0\left[1 - \dfrac{b^2\omega_p^2}{a'^2 u_0^2}\right]}$$

therefore $\left(\dfrac{\gamma_1+\gamma_2}{2}\right)\simeq\dfrac{\omega}{u_0}$ and the resultant wave has a phase velocity approximately equal to the beam velocity and an amplitude varying as $\cos\left[(\gamma_1-\gamma_2)/2\right]z$.

The maximum amplitude is therefore obtained when

$$z_0\left[(\gamma_1-\gamma_2)/2\right] = \pi/2$$

where z_0 is the optimum length of drift-tube.

The action of the drift-tube is described, in terms of a pure velocity-modulation theory, as follows. The velocity modulation produces a conduction current modulation. Because the modulated electrons retain their velocities, a very small amount of velocity modulation would eventually completely current modulate the beam.

The wave theory suggests that the velocity modulation and conduction current modulation vary as $\cos\left[(\gamma_1+\gamma_2)/2\right]z$ due to space charge and that there is no point in making the tube longer than z_0.

By combining the equations for γ_1 and γ_2, it is found that z_0 is proportional to a' and that the values of $\gamma_{1,2}$ are close together. We thus have a physical significance of a'.

We assumed $\omega/c < \gamma$ (i.e. if γ is real – waves with phase velocity $< c$). A similar analysis for the case of $\omega/c > \gamma$ could be made. However, waves with a phase velocity greater than c are usually only possible where the radius of the outer boundary is large enough to allow E_0 or H_0 waves.

Maxwell investigated the ionized layers of the atmosphere and, according to Hahn, concluded that two types of waves are possible.

(a) Waves in which most transfer of energy is in electromagnetic waves and electrons and ions play minor roles, and

(b) Waves in which most transfer of energy is in electron or ion movement and the velocity of propagation is low.

This appears to be the case in the present problem.

We have investigated (b) and have found that they have velocities very nearly equal to the beam velocity.

We have now completed Hahn's analysis indicating that perturbations can be propagated along electron beams by means of two unattenuated waves, one with phase velocity slightly less than the electron beam velocity and the other with phase velocity slightly greater than the electron beam velocity. The analysis is essentially a 'wave' theory and uses the electric and magnetic field and flux density vectors.

2.2.2.2. *The Ramo analysis*

An alternative 'wave' analysis, due to Ramo [12, 13], uses the electric scalar and magnetic vector potential.

From the relationship

$$\mathbf{E} = -\,\mathrm{grad}\,V - \mu_0\,\frac{\partial \mathbf{A}}{\partial t} \qquad\qquad 2.10$$

we get
$$\nabla^2 V - \frac{1}{c^2}\frac{\partial^2 V}{\partial t^2} = -\frac{\rho}{\varepsilon_0} \qquad \left(\text{using } \nabla\,.\,\mathbf{E} = \frac{\rho}{\varepsilon_0}\right).$$

For axial symmetry, this reduces to

$$\frac{\partial^2 V}{\partial r^2} + \frac{1}{r}\frac{\partial V}{\partial r} + (k^2 - \gamma^2)V = -\frac{\rho}{\varepsilon_0} \qquad\qquad 2.11$$

where $k = \omega/c$.

Now $\qquad \nabla . \mathbf{J} = -\partial\rho/\partial t \quad$ (The continuity equation)

and $\qquad \mathbf{J} = \rho_t \mathbf{u}$.

Considering motion in the z direction only we have

$$-\frac{\partial\rho}{\partial t} = \frac{\partial}{\partial z}(\rho_0 v_z + \rho u_0)$$

for small signals;

therefore $\qquad -j\omega\rho = -\rho_0 j\gamma v_z - u_0 j\gamma\rho$

therefore $\qquad \rho = \frac{\rho_0\gamma v_z}{(\omega - \gamma u_0)}$. $\hfill 2.12$

But $\qquad m\dfrac{dv_z}{dt} = -eE_z$

and $\qquad \dfrac{d}{dt} = j(\omega - \gamma u_0) \hfill$ (Eqn 1.2)

therefore $\qquad -\dfrac{e}{m}E_z = j(\omega - \gamma u_0)v_z$.

Eqn 2.10 gives

$$E_z = j(\gamma V - \mu_0\omega A_z)$$

but $\qquad \nabla . \mathbf{A} = -\varepsilon_0\dfrac{\partial V}{\partial t} \qquad\qquad \therefore A_z = \dfrac{\varepsilon_0\omega}{\gamma}V$.

$\therefore \qquad E_z = j\left(\gamma V - \dfrac{k^2}{\gamma}.V\right) \qquad\qquad = (\gamma^2 - k^2)\dfrac{jV}{\gamma}$

$\therefore \qquad v_z = \dfrac{-\eta}{j(\omega - \gamma u_0)}.\dfrac{jV}{\gamma}(\gamma^2 - k^2)$

$\therefore \qquad \rho = \dfrac{-\rho_0\gamma}{(\omega - \gamma u_0)^2}.\eta\dfrac{V}{\gamma}(\gamma^2 - k^2)$

$\therefore \qquad \rho = -\eta\rho_0\dfrac{(\gamma^2 - k^2)V}{(\omega - \gamma u_0)^2} = \dfrac{\varepsilon_0\omega_p^2}{(\omega - \gamma u_0)^2}(\gamma^2 - k^2)V$.

$\therefore$ Eqn 2.11 becomes

$$\frac{\partial^2 V}{\partial r^2} + \frac{1}{r}\frac{\partial V}{\partial r} + (k^2-\gamma^2)\left[1 - \frac{\omega_p^2}{(\omega-\gamma u_0)^2}\right]V = 0 .$$

The solutions assumed are:
for inside the beam

$$V_1 = A'J_0(Tr)$$

between beam and coaxial conducting cylinder

$$V_2 = C'\left[I_0(\tau r) + D'K_0(\tau r)\right]$$

where

$$T = \left\{(k^2-\gamma^2)\left[1 - \frac{\omega_p^2}{(\omega-\gamma u_0)^2}\right]\right\}^{\frac{1}{2}}$$ 2.13

and

$$\tau = (\gamma^2-k^2)^{\frac{1}{2}} .$$

At the conducting drift-tube, the tangential electric field = 0

therefore

$$D' = \frac{-I_0(\tau bR_1)}{K_0(\tau bR_1)}$$

where $bR_1 =$ radius of the drift-tube. At the surface of the beam, the tangential electric field is continuous and hence

$$\frac{A'}{C'} = \frac{I_0(\tau b) + D'K_0(\tau b)}{J_0(Tb)} .$$

Since only the z zomponent of $\mathbf{A}$ exists, only the θ component of $\mathbf{H}$ exists. This is continuous at the surface of the beam and requires $\partial A_z/\partial r$ and hence $\partial V/\partial r$, to be continuous at the same point. This gives

$$A'J_0'(Tb).(Tb) = C'\left[I_0'(\tau b) + D'K_0'(\tau b)\right](\tau b) .$$

Eliminating A'/C' and substituting $-J_1$ for J_0', I_1 for I_0' and $-K_1$ for K_0', gives

$$-(Tb)\frac{J_1(Tb)}{J_0(Tb)} = (\tau b)\frac{\left[I_1(\tau b) - D'K_1(\tau b)\right]}{\left[I_0(\tau b) + D'K_0(\tau b)\right]} .$$ 2.14

In order to find the value of γ for the space-charge waves, note from

Eqn 2.13 that T varies rapidly near $\gamma = \gamma_0 (= \omega/u_0)$ due to the term $(\omega - \gamma u_0)^2$ but that τ is not greatly affected by small changes in γ near $\gamma = \gamma_0$. We recall (Section 2.2.2.1) that for space-charge waves $\gamma = \gamma_0 (1 \pm \delta)$ i.e. $\gamma \simeq \gamma_0$, since δ is very small. Therefore in the right-hand side of Eqn 2.14 we may substitute γ_0 for γ without a loss of accuracy and this may be regarded as known for a given set of boundary conditions (tube parameters).

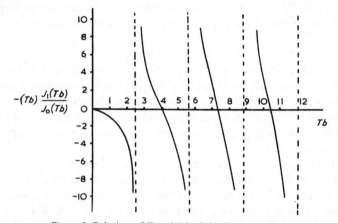

Figure 5. Solution of Eqn 2.14 of the Ramo analysis

We therefore only need to plot $-(Tb)[J_1(Tb)]/[J_0(Tb)]$. This is shown in Figure 5. The R.H.S. of Eqn 2.14 has an infinite number of intersections with this curve. For each of these values of (Tb)

$$\frac{T^2}{(\gamma^2 - k^2)} = \left\{ \frac{\omega_p^2}{(\omega - \gamma u_0)^2} - 1 \right\}. \qquad 2.15$$

Putting $\gamma = \gamma_0$ and using $\gamma^2 \gg k^2$ we have

$$(\omega - \gamma u_0)^2 = \frac{\omega_p^2 \gamma_0^2}{(T^2 + \gamma_0^2)} = \frac{\omega_p^2 \omega^2}{(T^2 u_0^2 + \omega^2)} = \omega^2 \delta_1^2$$

therefore $\qquad \gamma = \dfrac{\omega}{u_0}(1 \pm \delta_1) = \gamma_0 (1 \pm \delta_1) \qquad\qquad 2.16$

where
$$\delta_1 = \left\{ \frac{\omega_p^2}{(\omega^2 + T^2 u_0^2)} \right\}^{\frac{1}{2}}.$$

Eqn 2.16 gives

$$\gamma = \frac{\omega}{u_0} \pm \frac{\omega_p}{u_0 \left[1 + \dfrac{T^2}{\gamma_0^2} \right]^{\frac{1}{2}}}. \qquad 2.17$$

We see therefore that again we have two unattenuated space-charge waves with phase velocities very close to the electron beam velocity.

2.2.2.3. *Discussion of the Hahn-Ramo theory*

The analysis given by Hahn, was undoubtedly a great step forward in the efforts to understand the mechanism of the velocity-modulation tube. Only a few months before the publication of the theory, Hahn and Metcalf [5] described a velocity-modulation tube. They derived expressions for a few tube parameters but neglected some important space-charge effects.

Hahn used the obvious approach, namely the use of Maxwell's equations. This is a difficult method and one that has its limitations, because, as we have seen, even though only a small-signal analysis was made, a general solution is not possible. Also, it is difficult to chose assumptions that do not violate Maxwell's equations. For example, we cannot assume that, in the absence of a signal, the velocity-modulation tube consists of a beam of electrons of uniform charge density and velocity drifting down the axis of a cylindrical conducting tube, without further qualification. One could consider which distribution of charge and velocity must exist in the absence of a signal, but this will be so dependant on tube geometry and other parameters as to be inapplicable in the general case.

Ramo also used Maxwell's equations but introduced the magnetic vector potential concept. He made no attempt to produce a general solution, but introduced the assumption that there was no electron motion in any direction other than that of the electron flow, at the beginning of the analysis. He also introduced additional boundary conditions qualifying the assumption that in the absence of waves, the beam has uniform distribution of charge density and axial velocity.

So for as the assumptions are concerned, one of the biggest restrictions and deviation from practice is probably assumption (a) (Section 2.2.1), namely, a.c. values are very small compared to d.c. values. However, since the known phenomena obtained in the multitude of practical devices now in use throughout the World can be explained qualitatively in terms of the space-charge-wave theory, which almost always incorporates this assumption, it is fair to assume that this is a valid assumption. One may, however, have reservations about its validity when considering increasing (growing) space-charge waves. Assumption (b), the radius of the electron beam is held constant, simplifies the theory considerably and although the electron beam in devices is probably not of constant radius this is a resonable assumption. The effect of having a d.c. magnetic field of lesser magnitude is investigated in Section 2.3 onwards. In this chapter we are solely concerned with cases in which the velocity of electrons is single valued. The effects of multivelocity electron beams are considered in Chapter 4. Positive ion neutralization (assumption (f)) is assumed for convenience. The direct-current charge density due to the electrons is supposed to be neutralized exactly by that due to the positive ions, so that in the absence of a signal there is no steady electric field, no d.c. charge density, no direct current and no steady magnetic field due to the beam. Coupled with assumption (g), the positive ions have infinite mass and therefore no a.c. motion, this enables us to consider only the r.f. space-charge effects of the electrons. It is interesting to note that these two assumptions (f and g) were almost always assumed in the early years of the evolution of space-charge-wave theory. More recently, however, it appears to have become the practice merely to assume that the d.c. effects are balanced out without assuming positive ion neutralization, and Hutter [11] does not even mention this point. Since in most practical cases $u_0 \ll c/10$ assumption (h), the velocity of electrons is very much less than the velocity of light, is quite reasonable and the relativistic case is not considered.

The basic assumptions were used by both workers and we have seen that they achieved the same result using slightly different methods. Let us now compare and contrast their methods.

Hahn used the general solution of Maxwell's equations, but found that the mathematics was becoming so unweildy that simplifications had to be made and he introduced $\omega_c = \infty$, $\omega/c < \gamma$ and the radius of the beam $= b$. Ramo, having had the benefit of Hahn's experience and advice, was able to make use of the knowledge that $\gamma \simeq \gamma_0$ which, together with the other assumptions, greatly simplifies the analysis. He did, however, attempt to consider the 'higher orders' which were not considered by Hahn, but it appears that Hahn was aware of their significance.

By putting

$$V_1 = A'_n J_n(Tr) e^{jn\theta}$$

and

$$V_2 = C'_n [I_n(\tau r) + D' K_n(\tau r)]$$

he obtained an equation similar to Eqn 2.14 in $J_n(Tb)$, $I_n(\tau b)$ and $K_n(\tau b)$. Thus the values of γ for each order of wave are obtainable.

The methods these workers used to find the values of γ differed. The Hahn method has advantages if one is more concerned with designing tubes, since the parameter a', which figures prominently in the analysis, is related to optimum drift-tube length. The Ramo method, on the other hand, was used because the primary purpose of the work at this stage was to demonstrate the possibility of the existence of waves and his method was much simpler. One can also argue it is less open to criticism. The Hahn method depended on the assumption that a' was constant and one is left to deduce from Figure 4 that this is so. Since the curves given are said to be for a typical case and no values of beam current, voltage or any other variable were given, this is not very satisfactory. It was also assumed that $(\omega_p b / a' u_0) \ll 1$. Since we can take $a' \simeq 1$ (from case given in Figure 4) we have that $(\omega_p b / u_0) \ll 1$. But

$$\frac{\omega_p b}{u_0} = \sqrt{\left(\frac{ne^2}{m\varepsilon_0}\right)} \frac{b}{u_0} = \sqrt{\left(\frac{1 \cdot 759 \times 10^{11}}{8 \cdot 85 \times 10^{-12}}\right)} \frac{10b}{2 \cdot 99 \times 10^8} \rho_0^{\frac{1}{2}}$$

(assuming $u_0 = c/10$) and if $b = 0 \cdot 01$ m, we have $\sqrt{(2)} \times 3 \cdot 3 \, . \, 10 \rho_0^{\frac{1}{2}}$ and this must be $\ll 1$.

Therefore $\rho_0 \ll 4 \cdot 5 \times 10^{-4}$ coulombs/m^3 if this condition is satisfied. We are, therefore, left to conclude that this is a reasonable assumption since a typical value of ρ_0 might be $1 \cdot 5 \times 10^{-5}$ coloumbs/m³ which satisfies this condition.

While we are only concerned with space-charge waves in which $\gamma \simeq \gamma_0$, it is interesting to note that there are also solutions to Eqn 2.15 for which γ is far removed from γ_0. Suppose $\gamma \ll \gamma_0$ then $(\omega - \gamma u_0)^2 \simeq \omega^2$. Since $\omega_p^2/\omega^2 < 1$ for electron beams, Eqn 2.15 gives

$$T^2 = (k^2 - \gamma^2) \times \text{(a positive quantity)} .$$

Therefore, there are solutions for which $\gamma^2 \ll k^2$, which is the case referred to on p. 18; these are sometimes called field waves. Eqn 2.15 becomes

$$T^2 = (k^2 - \gamma^2) \times \left(1 - \frac{\omega_p^2}{\omega^2} \right) \qquad 2.18$$

and this indicates that there is a frequency corresponding to each value of T^2 below which γ^2 becomes negative and imaginary. Since γ has only an imaginary part, a wave does not propagate. Eqn 2.18 shows that the cut-off frequency ω_{cu} is given by

$$\omega_{cu}^2 = \omega_p^2 + T^2 c^2 .$$

At the cut-off point, $\gamma = 0$ and the wave velocity is infinite. It is not intended to discuss these waves any further.

We have now developed the theory for a finite beam in a coaxial conducting cylinder and arrived at equations for the propagation constants of two unattenuated space-charge waves. It will be appreciated that this system is of considerable interest, because it closely resembles practical devices and it is no doubt for this reason that this problem was attacked first. It is, however, instructive to consider the case of the infinite beam and then to compare the two cases.

2.2.3. Beams of infinite cross-section

The method used was designed by Pierce [15].

The equations required are

$$\nabla . \mathbf{E} = \rho/\varepsilon_0 \qquad \text{(Poisson)}$$

$$m(d\mathbf{u}/dt) = -e\mathbf{E} \qquad \text{(Motion)}$$

$$\nabla . \mathbf{J} = -\partial\rho/\partial t \qquad \text{(Charge conservation)}$$

and
$$\mathbf{J} = \rho_t \mathbf{u} \qquad \text{(Conduction current)}$$

On linearizing, these equations become (omitting the suffix z)

$$-j\gamma E = \rho/\varepsilon_0 \qquad \qquad 2.19$$

$$mj(\omega - \gamma u_0)v = -eE \qquad \qquad 2.20$$

$$-j\gamma J = -j\omega\rho \qquad \qquad 2.21$$

$$J = (\rho_0 v + \rho u_0) \qquad \qquad 2.22$$

Note Eqn 2.20 uses Eqn 1.2

$$d/dt = j(\omega - \gamma u_0)$$

and du/dt is the rate of change of u with respect to t for a single electron i.e. du/dt observed by an observer moving with the electron.

Eqns 2.19 and 2.21 give

$$J/E = -j\omega\varepsilon_0 \qquad \qquad 2.23$$

(this represents the field induced in free space by conduction current density J).

Eqns 2.22 and 2.21 give

$$J = \rho_0 v + \gamma\frac{J}{\omega}u_0$$

therefore
$$v = \frac{J}{\rho_0}\left\{1 - \frac{\gamma}{\omega}u_0\right\}.$$

Therefore from Eqn 2.20 we have

$$v = -\frac{eE}{mj(\omega - \gamma u_0)} = \frac{J}{\rho_0}\left\{1 - \frac{\gamma}{\omega}u_0\right\} \qquad \qquad 2.24$$

therefore
$$\frac{J}{E} = j\frac{e}{m}\rho_0\frac{\omega}{(\omega - \gamma u_0)^2}. \qquad \qquad 2.25$$

Combining Eqns 2.23 and 2.25 gives

$$-j\omega\varepsilon_0 = j\eta\rho_0 \frac{\omega}{(\omega - \gamma u_0)^2}$$

therefore
$$1 = \frac{\omega_p^2}{(\omega - \gamma u_0)^2}. \qquad 2.26$$

Thus we have the dispersion equation: the relationship between ω and γ

$$\gamma = \frac{\omega \pm \omega_p}{u_0} \qquad 2.27$$

We see that γ is real and so there are two simple unattenuated waves. Since the phase velocity $u_p = \omega/\gamma$

$$u_p = \frac{u_0}{\left(1 \pm \dfrac{\omega_p}{\omega}\right)}$$

therefore
$$u_{p(s)} = \frac{u_0}{\left(1 + \dfrac{\omega_p}{\omega}\right)}$$

and
$$u_{p(f)} = \frac{u_0}{\left(1 - \dfrac{\omega_p}{\omega}\right)}. \qquad 2.28$$

Since $\omega_p \ll \omega$ (Section 1.2.2) the phase velocity of one wave is slightly slower than the velocity of the electron beam ($u_{p(s)}$), and the phase velocity of the other wave is slightly faster than the velocity of the electron beam ($u_{p(f)}$). It is because the phase velocities of these waves are so close to the velocity of the electron beam and this velocity is usually slow compared to the velocity of light, that space-charge waves are often called 'slow' waves. Care must be taken not to confuse the phrase 'slow wave' in this context with the 'slow space-charge wave' which refers to the slower of the two space-charge waves. The group velocity is discussed in Section 2.2.5.

Eqns 2.28 also show that if the electrons are not moving ($u_0 = 0$) then space-charge waves do not travel; in other words, space-charge waves travel with the electron beam and not through it.

Comparison of Eqns 2.17 and 2.27 shows that if we put

$$\frac{\omega_p}{\left(1 + \dfrac{T^2}{\gamma_0^2}\right)^{\frac{1}{2}}} = \omega_q ,$$

these two equations become identical in form. It seems reasonable to conclude, therefore, that the effect of reducing the diameter of the beam, coupled with placing it in a coaxial conducting cylinder, is merely to produce a plasma frequency which is less than ω_p. Thus ω_q is called the effective plasma frequency. We proceed to discuss the factors that produce this reduction in plasma frequency.

Before doing so, however, let us note that this method of Pierce does not use the wave equations of Maxwell. It is possible to develop space-charge-wave theory by this method and this is known as the electronic or ballistic theory. Hutter [11] also uses this method, but it does not give any indication of the r.f. frequency limits beyond which the theory does not apply; only the wave theory gives information on this effect.

A detailed derivation of space-charge waves using the electronic theory is given in Appendix 2.

2.2.4. Plasma frequency reduction factors

In a finite electron beam, the longitudinal electric field is decreased (with respect to the field in the infinite electron beam) due to fringing effects which are dependent on the presence of conducting walls, helices or other surfaces as well as the geometry of the system. Consequently, the plasma oscillation frequency is reduced and the reduced plasma frequency, usually called the effective plasma frequency ω_q, is an important parameter in the design of microwave devices.

The theory for the finite electron beam, as derived in Section 2.2.2, involves the solution of Maxwell's equations and boundary conditions are applied, thus, taking into account the effect of beam size and, in this case, the effect of having a coaxial conducting drift-tube surrounding the beam.

We found that

$$\gamma = \frac{\omega}{u_0} \pm \frac{\omega_p}{u_0 \left[1 + \dfrac{T^2}{\gamma_0^2}\right]^{\frac{1}{2}}} .$$ (Eqn 2.17)

The first term of the right-hand side of the equation, (ω/u_0), indicates a phase shift due to the d.c. transit angle. The second term is a phase shift due to the space-charge and this is a function of the geometry of the system.

Now let
$$\gamma = \frac{\omega}{u_0} \pm \frac{\omega_q}{u_0}$$

where ω_q is defined by

$$\frac{\omega_q}{\omega_p} = \frac{1}{\left[1 + \dfrac{T^2}{\gamma_0^2}\right]^{\frac{1}{2}}} = R .$$ 2.29

R is known as the plasma frequency reduction factor. We can simply replace ω_p in any equations for the propagation of space-charge waves in infinite beams by ω_q in order to make the equations applicable to finite beams and their systems. Also, since the second term in the expression for γ

$$\frac{\omega_p}{u_0 \left[1 + \dfrac{T^2}{\gamma_0^2}\right]^{\frac{1}{2}}}$$

is proportional to $\{J_0/[1 + (T^2/\gamma_0^2)]\}^{\frac{1}{2}}$, we see that the phase shift due to the space-charge is governed by an effective d.c. current density $J_{0(e)}$. Similarly one can replace J_0 by $J_{0(e)}$ in the propagation equations for infinite beams to enable one to apply them to finite systems. Now put the radius of the drift-tube equal to bR_1 (p. 20) and this is equal to a.

Therefore $\qquad\qquad R_1 = a/b \qquad$ (note R_1 is always $\geqslant 1$) .

In the development of the Ramo theory, for a given set of boundary conditions (and this includes R_1) a set of values of (Tb) is found, each of which satisfies Eqn 2.15, and for each value of (Tb) in this set, two unattenuated space-charge waves are propagated.

Suppose, therefore, that $(Tb) = x$ where x is obtained from Figure 5 combined with the R.H.S. of Eqn 2.14 (i.e. L.H.S. of 2.14 $\equiv$ R.H.S. of 2.14), and is known.

Therefore
$$\frac{T}{\gamma_0} = \frac{x}{\gamma_0 b}$$

Since x is known, it is possible to select values of $(\gamma_0 b)$ and find the corresponding values of (T/γ_0) for any value of R_1 selected, and also for each pair of space-charge waves (i.e. different values of (Tb) – the various orders of waves). The curves for $R_1 = 1$, 3 and ∞, for a solid cylindrical electron beam in a coaxial conducting cylinder, were calculated by Parzen [16] and are reproduced in Figure 6. Having ascertained values

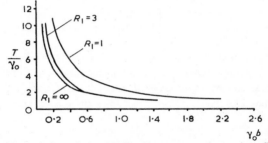

Figure 6. The variation of phase shift, due to space-charge, in a finite solid cylindrical electron beam in rectilinear flow, in a coaxial conducting cylinder

of (T/γ_0) for selected values of $(\gamma_0 b)$ it is a simple matter to obtain corresponding values of R from Eqn 2.29. Such curves take the form of those shown in Figure 7.

It is possible to produce curves of this form directly, by choosing a value of $(\gamma_0 b)$ and calculating the R.H.S. of Eqn 2.14 for a given value of R_1 (assuming $\gamma^2 \gg k^2$ and $\gamma \simeq \gamma_0$). This gives the value of (Tb) directly and R is obtained from Eqn 2.29. Watkins [17] and Sullivan [18] calculated graphs by this method.

By considering a special case, that when $R_1 = 1$, i.e. when the beam fills the tube, one interesting feature of the finite beam case is highlighted.

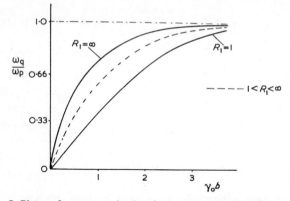

Figure 7. Plasma frequency reduction factors for a solid cylindrical electron beam in rectilinear flow, in a coaxial conducting cylinder

If $R_1 = 1$, the R.H.S. of Eqn 2.14 $= \infty$. Therefore $J_0(Tb) = 0$.

Tables of Bessel functions [Jahnke and Emde, 19] show that $Tb = 2.405$. Therefore in this case

$$\left(\frac{2.405}{\gamma_0 b}\right)^2 = \left[\left(\frac{\omega_p}{\omega_q}\right)^2 - 1\right] \qquad \text{(Eqn 2.29)}$$

Therefore:

if $\gamma_0 b = 0$, $\omega_q/\omega_p = 0$

if $\gamma_0 b = 1$, $\omega_q/\omega_p = 0.335$

if $\gamma_0 b = 2.405$, $\omega_q/\omega_p = 0.707$

and if $\gamma_0 b = \infty$ $\omega_q/\omega_p = 1.0$.

From these figures the form of the R *versus* $\gamma_0 b$ curve is easily obtained. Note that it was assumed that $\gamma \simeq \gamma_0$ throughout and that any one graph applies only to a specific order of space-charge waves.

Also, for small values of $(\gamma_0 b)$

$$(\omega_q/\omega_p) \propto \gamma_0 b \,.$$

But $$\gamma_0 b = (\omega/u_0).\, b$$

therefore $$\gamma_0 b \propto \omega$$

therefore $$\omega_q \propto \omega \,.$$

But $$u_p = \frac{u_0}{\left(1 \pm \dfrac{\omega_q}{\omega}\right)}$$

therefore $$u_p = \text{constant} \,.$$

Thus we have a dispersion free system, i.e. u_p is independent of ω. It will be seen later (Section 2.2.5) that in the infinite beam the waves are dispersive waves, and so one can conclude that one effect of reducing the diameter of the beam, and at the same time confining it in a coaxial conducting drift-tube, is to make the space-charge waves disperse less. Note that the dispersion free case above is only for $R_1 = 1$, and, that as the beam diameter decreases so $\omega_q/\omega_p \to 1$; consequently as the beam diameter increases the effect of geometry increases.

Branch and Mihran [20] have calculated plasma frequency reduction factors for a variety of electron beam shapes and drift-tube dimensions. They have plotted these *versus* $\gamma_0 b$ and R is also plotted as a function of $1/R_1$ with $\gamma_0 b$ as a parameter. The curves for a solid cylindrical beam in a coaxial conducting drift-tube are shown in Figures 8a and 8b.

Branch [21] has suggested that the effect of finite geometry is more important than the presence of a conductor. To support this theory, plasma frequency reduction factors have been calculated for a solid beam surrounded by a solid drift-tube and also by a helix. It is found that there is very little difference in the values of R obtained in both these cases particularly for values of $1/R_1 < \frac{1}{2}$, *i.e.* for $a > 2b$, the beam half filling the tube (see Figure 9). As Birdsall and Schumacher [22] have pointed out care should be taken not to assume that this is also the case in magnetic field strengths less than infinite.

In order to pursue this point further one would have to introduce the

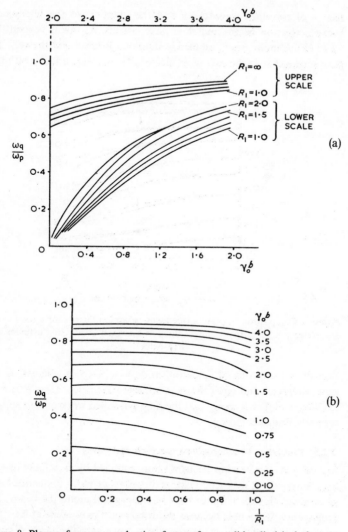

Figure 8. Plasma frequency reduction factors for a solid cylindrical electron beam in rectilinear flow, in a coaxial conducting cylinder

theory of travelling-wave tubes and the question of the interaction between electron beams and slow wave circuits. As this is beyond the scope of this monograph, we merely state that Birdsall and Brewer [23] have shown that in the case of an electron beam inside a helix, with the

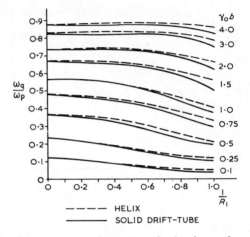

Figure 9. Comparison of plasma frequency reduction factors for a solid cylindrical electron beam in rectilinear flow, in a coaxial conducting cylinder and in a helix

electron velocity out of synchronism $\omega_q/\omega = \sqrt{(4QC^3)}$ where C is the gain parameter and (QC) the space-charge parameter. Thus R can be calculated. Suffice it to say that the little published work on this subject supports Branch's theory.

2.2.5. Properties of longitudinal space-charge waves

In summary, if a moving electron beam, confined by an infinite or very high longitudinal magnetic field, is disturbed at radio frequencies at a given point this disturbance may be propagated along the beam. The propagation is possible because the disturbance may excite at least two unattenuated space-charge waves which move with the electron beam.

It is appropriate to point out here that these waves must first be excited before they can be propagated. This fact was obviously appreciated by Hahn but it would appear that it was not appreciated by many other workers for some years. To excite waves, one can apply an accelerating voltage gradient to a short length of the beam by applying a potential difference across a gap in the conducting cylinder. This imparts a velocity modulation to the beam assumed to be uniform over the cross-section of the beam.

The two space-charge waves differ in their phase velocities; one has a phase velocity slightly less than the electron beam velocity and the other has a phase velocity slightly greater than the electron beam velocity. For the infinite beam, the phase velocities are functions of ω, i.e. they are dispersive waves. Also, since the group velocity u_g is given by

$$u_g = \partial \omega / \partial \beta,$$

$u_g = u_0$ for both the fast and the slow waves (ω_p is assumed constant), and this is another indication that space-charge waves are convected with the beam and not propagated through it. It is seen that in this case the phase and group velocities are different.

The two waves also differ in the phase angles that exist between the velocity modulation and the conduction current modulation, due to the conditions of excitation.

Since
$$\nabla . \mathbf{J} = -\partial \rho / \partial t$$

and
$$\gamma = \gamma_0(1 \pm \delta_1), \tag{Eqn 2.16}$$

$$-j\gamma J = -j\omega\rho$$

therefore
$$J = u_0 \rho / (1 \pm \delta_1).$$

Since
$$J = \rho_0 v + \rho u_0$$

$$Jv = -\rho_0(\pm \delta_1). \tag{2.30}$$

Hence, if δ_1 is negative – the fast wave – the current density modulation and the velocity modulation are in phase, whilst if δ_1 is positive – the slow wave – the current density modulation and the velocity modulation are π radians out of phase. Thus, if the two waves propagate together their velocity modulations add at some parts of the beam and subtract at others. Similarly for the current density modulations. Where the velocity modulations add, the current density modulations subtract and where the velocities subtract the currents add. The optimum drift-tube length z_0 is where, the distance from the point at which the velocities are a maximum and $J = 0$, to the point at which the currents are a maximum is an odd number of $\pi/2$ radians, i.e. $z_0 = \pi/2\gamma_0\delta_1$.

Eqn 2.30 gives

$$\left(\frac{\rho_0 v + \rho u_0}{v} \right) = \frac{-\rho_0}{(\pm \delta_1)} ,$$

therefore
$$\frac{\rho}{\rho_0} = -\left[\frac{1}{(\pm \delta_1)} + 1 \right] \frac{v}{u_0} ;$$

for the fast wave, δ_1 is negative,

therefore
$$\frac{\rho_f}{\rho_0} = -\left[\frac{1}{-\delta_1} + 1 \right] \frac{v_f}{u_0} \simeq \frac{1}{\delta_1} \frac{v_f}{u_0} , \qquad 2.31$$

for the slow wave, δ_1 is positive,

therefore
$$\frac{\rho_s}{\rho_0} = -\left[\frac{1}{\delta_1} + 1 \right] \frac{v_s}{u_0} \simeq \frac{-1}{\delta_1} \frac{v_s}{u_0} \qquad 2.32$$

where the subscripts f and s refer to fast and slow waves respectively. Therefore, in the fast wave the charge density modulation is in phase with the velocity modulation, and in the slow wave the charge density modulation is out of phase with the velocity modulation by π radians. Thus, for the fast wave, more than the average number of electrons travel at a velocity greater than the average velocity and less than the average number of electrons travel at a velocity less than the average velocity. Therefore, a beam with a fast wave has more kinetic energy than it possesses when the fast wave is not propagated. The converse is true for the slow wave. Consequently, to propagate a fast wave, energy must be added to the beam and to propagate a slow wave, energy must be removed from the beam (or negative energy has to be added to the beam). Both waves can be propagated without adding any energy.

This is an extremely important property of space-charge waves.

Although it is not proposed to pursue the question of the energy of space-charge waves at this stage, we will digress a little to introduce a concept of Pierce's [15].

Two forms of energy are of primary importance in the waves.

(1) The variation of electrostatic energy associated with the bunching of electrons and

(2) The variation of kinetic energy associated with differences in the velocities of the electrons.

The waves may, therefore, be called electro-mechanical waves; the electrical energy associated with transmission lines and wave guides is present but the magnetic energy is replaced by the kinetic energy (we have neglected the magnetic energy by neglecting the magnetic field due to the beam because $u_0 \ll c$).

We now have sufficient information to enable us to draw a physical picture of space-charge waves. A disturbance at radio frequencies may be propagated along a moving electron beam by means of two waves which form an interference pattern. They do not propagate *through* the beam but the beam is a medium capable of supporting them. Each electron in the beam is set vibrating separately at an angular frequency ω_p (the natural frequency of oscillations of electrons in a given plasma) about its equilibrium position, but with different phases and amplitudes to produce the effect of a wave as viewed by a stationary observer. The phase relationships between the vibrating electrons and amplitudes of vibration depend on the way they are set vibrating. Since the electrons can only have a frequency ω_p, seen by an observer moving with the velocity of the beam, the frequency ω of the space-charge waves, seen by a stationary observer, is a Doppler shifted frequency of the plasma frequency ω_p. We can see, therefore, that the phrase 'electro-mechanical wave' is an excellent description of a space-charge wave. It not only gives an insight to the physical nature of such a wave but also distinguishes it from, and draws an analogy with, the electro-magnetic wave.

One should point out that Harman [24] gave an analogy between space-charge waves in an electron beam and sound waves in a gas. Unfortunately, there are some essential differences between electrons in a beam and a gas, and, as we have seen, space-charge waves are dispersive waves; sound waves are non-dispersive waves. Also, for space-charge waves the electron beam must be moving, for sound waves the gas may be stationary. The analogy should be viewed with care.

Finally, both the Hahn and Ramo analyses indicate that there are an infinite number of pairs of space-charge waves. Our discussion on the properties of these waves applies to both first order and higher order waves. Of course, the values of the parameters will vary since they depend on δ_1 (or δ) which in turn depends on T. We are mainly concerned with the amplitudes of the excited waves which are discussed briefly in Appendix 6. Suffice it to say at this stage that it is found that the amplitude of the higher order waves excited is usually small compared with the amplitude of the first order wave.

The theory applies exclusively to beams in an infinite or very high longitudinal magnetic field which is probably the most important case. (A more precise definition of 'very high' is given in Section 2.4.4.) It is, however, interesting to see how the theory has to be modified for other values of longitudinal magnetic field. Let us first of all discuss briefly the case in which there is a 'Brillouin' longitudinal magnetic field.

2.3 PROPAGATION IN BRILLOUIN LONGITUDINAL MAGNETIC FIELDS

2.3.1. Definition of Brillouin field and Brillouin flow

In view of the confusion that exists in the literature, it is important to state precisely the author's understanding and usage of the phrases Brillouin field and Brillouin flow.

Busch's theorem states that:

'If an electron is emitted from a plane with negligible angular momentum, and it then moves in an axially symmetric field to arrive at a second plane, which is parallel to the plane from which it was emitted, the angular momentum is conserved.'

In terms of the magnetic flux ϕ flowing through these two planes (1 and 2) this means that, for paraxial electrons

$$\left(\frac{d\theta}{dt}\right)_2 = \frac{e}{2m}\left(\frac{1}{\pi r_2^2}\right)(\phi_2 - \phi_1)$$

where the suffices 1 and 2 refer to planes 1 and 2 respectively. If we now make plane 1 the cathode of the system and plane 2, parallel to the cathode, a plane in the electron beam in the drift-tube, then

$$\left(\frac{d\theta}{dt}\right)_2 = \frac{e}{2m}\left(\frac{1}{\pi r^2}\right)(\pi r^2 B_{z0} - \pi r_c^2 B_c)$$

where r_c = radius of the cathode

B_{z0} = longitudinal flux density threading the plane under consideration.

B_c = longitudinal flux density threading the cathode.

Therefore
$$\dot\theta_0 = \frac{e}{2m} B_{z0}\left[1 - \frac{r_c^2}{r^2}\frac{B_c}{B_{z0}}\right]$$

therefore
$$\dot\theta_0 = \omega_L(1-K) \qquad\qquad 2.33$$

where ω_L = Lamor angular frequency ($=eB_{z0}/2m$) and

$$K = \frac{r_c^2 B_c}{r^2 B_{z0}}. \qquad\qquad 2.34$$

Consider now the case in which the cathode is completely shielded from any magnetic field and the electron beam enters, abruptly, a region containing a magnetic field B_B such that there is no d.c. radial velocity.

This, as we see from Eqns 2.33 and 2.34, gives $K=0$ and thus $\dot\theta_0 = \omega_L$. For the purpose of this monograph, we will define this as being the 'Brillouin flow' condition and the magnetic field B_B into which the electron beam abruptly enters as the 'Brillouin field'. One may feel that this is a condition that is very difficult to achieve in practice. However, the simplification in the mathematics obtained by having $\dot\theta_0$ constant makes it easier to gain an insight into the physical phenomena occurring in systems in which the longitudinal magnetic field is not infinite. It is for this reason that we treat this special case before proceeding to cases in which the longitudinal magnetic field strength is arbitrary.

2.3.2. Assumptions

In the case of Brillouin flow, certain assumptions made in Section 2.2 no longer hold because the longitudinal magnetic field is insufficient to keep the radius of the electron beam constant. Consequently the electrons have radial velocity and radial charge displacements. The other assumptions made in the rectiliner flow case are still utilized.

To facilitate manipulation, the perturbed radius is assumed to be given by

$$r = r_0 + \hat{r}_1 \, e^{j(\omega t - \gamma z)} = r_0 + r_1$$

and the rippled beam is assumed to be equivalent to a uniform cylindrical beam with an a.c. surface charge density $\rho_0 r_1$ or a surface current line-density whose components are

$$G_z = \rho_0 r_1 u_0$$
$$G_\theta = \rho_0 r_1 \dot{\theta}_0 b = \rho_0 r_1 \omega_L b \, .$$

Figure 10 illustrates this assumption.

RECTILINEAR EQUIVALENT BEAM

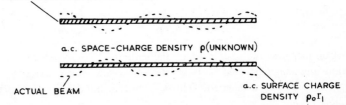

a.c. SPACE-CHARGE DENSITY ρ(UNKNOWN)

ACTUAL BEAM

a.c. SURFACE CHARGE DENSITY $\rho_0 r_1$

Figure 10. Illustration of the assumption that a rippled beam can be replaced by an equivalent rectilinear beam with a.c. surface charge density

The interior of the beam has an unknown a.c. space-charge density ρ. In other words, the boundary disturbance is replaced by an equivalent surface charge density or a surface current line-density keeping the interior of the beam as for the rectiliner beam case.

2.3.3. The analysis

A similar method to that adopted by Hahn (Section 2.2.2.1) gives the following equations (see Appendix 3).

For the 'E$_0$' wave (H$_z$=0)

$$\frac{1}{r} \frac{\partial}{\partial r}\left(r \frac{\partial E_z}{\partial r}\right) - \gamma^2 E_z = \frac{\gamma^2}{j\omega\varepsilon_0} J_z + \frac{\gamma}{\varepsilon_0 \omega} \cdot \frac{1}{r} \frac{\partial}{\partial r}(rJ_r) \qquad \text{2.35 (A3.8)}$$

$$E_r = \frac{j}{\gamma} \frac{\partial E_z}{\partial r} \qquad \text{2.36 (A3.7)}$$

$$H_\theta = \frac{\omega\varepsilon_0}{\gamma} E_r - \frac{j}{\gamma} J_r . \qquad \text{2.37 (A3.6)}$$

For the 'H$_0$' wave (E$_z$=0)

$$\frac{1}{r} \frac{\partial}{\partial r}\left(r \frac{\partial H_z}{\partial r}\right) - \gamma^2 H_z = - \frac{1}{r} \frac{\partial}{\partial r}(rJ_\theta) \qquad \text{2.38 (A3.12)}$$

$$H_r = j\gamma\left(\frac{\partial H_z}{\partial r} + J_\theta\right) \qquad \text{2.39 (A3.14)}$$

$$E_\theta = - \frac{\omega\mu_0}{\gamma} \cdot H_r \qquad \text{2.40 (A3.13)}$$

The equations of motion of a single electron in a d.c. axial magnetic flux density B_{z0} give (see Appendix 4):

$$r_1 = \frac{\eta E_r}{(\omega - \gamma u_0)^2} \qquad \text{2.41}$$

$$\theta_1 = 0 \qquad \text{2.42}$$

$$z_1 = \frac{\eta E_z}{(\omega - \gamma u_0)^2} . \qquad \text{2.43}$$

Therefore the total d.c. velocity $\bar{u}_0$ is given by co-ordinates

$$\bar{u}_0 = (0, r\dot{\theta}_0, u_0)$$

and the total a.c. velocity $\bar{v}$ is given by co-ordinates

$$\bar{v} = (\dot{r}_1, r\dot{\theta}_1, \dot{z}_1).$$

Therefore $\qquad \bar{v} = j(\omega - \gamma u_0)(r_1, r\theta_1, z_1) \qquad \text{2.44}$

Eqn 2.44 combined with Eqns 2.41 to 2.43 becomes

$$\bar{v} = \frac{j\eta}{(\omega - \gamma u_0)} [E_r, 0, E_z]$$

but we know

$$\rho = \frac{j\rho_0}{(\omega - \gamma u_0)} \nabla \cdot \bar{v} \qquad \text{(Eqn A3.16)}$$

therefore $$\rho = \frac{j\rho_0}{(\omega - \gamma u_0)} \cdot \frac{j\eta}{(\omega - \gamma u_0)} \nabla \cdot \mathbf{E}$$

therefore $$\rho = \frac{\omega_p^2}{(\omega - \gamma u_0)^2} \cdot \rho$$

and for this to be true we must have either

(i) $$\frac{\omega_p^2}{(\omega - \gamma u_0)^2} = 1 \quad \text{or} \qquad 2.45$$

(ii) $$\rho = 0. \qquad 2.46$$

Eqn 2.45 is the intrinsic solution and gives two unattenuated space-charge waves as in the infinite rectiliner beam case,

$$\gamma_{1,2} = \frac{\omega}{u_0} \pm \frac{\omega_p}{u_0}.$$

Further reference to this solution is postponed until Section 2.4.5.2.

Eqn 2.46 is of particular interest. It can be used to obtain the components of the total convection current density **J** and the components can be substituted into the wave equations.

Now $$\mathbf{J} = \rho_0 \bar{v} + \rho \bar{u}_0$$

therefore $$J_r = \rho_0 v_r$$

$$= \rho_0 j(\omega - \gamma u_0) r_1 \qquad \text{(from 2.44)}$$

$$= \rho_0 j(\omega - \gamma u_0) \frac{\eta E_r}{(\omega - \gamma u_0)^2}. \qquad \text{(from 2.41)}$$

But
$$E_r = \frac{j}{\gamma} \frac{\partial E_z}{\partial r} \qquad \text{(from 2.36)}$$

therefore
$$J_r = \frac{\omega_p^2 \varepsilon_0}{(\omega - \gamma u_0)\gamma} \cdot \frac{\partial E_z}{\partial r} \qquad 2.47$$

also
$$J_\theta = 0$$

and
$$J_z = \rho_0 v_z$$

therefore
$$J_z = -\frac{j\omega_p^2 \varepsilon_0}{(\omega - \gamma u_0)} \cdot E_z .$$

Substituting J_z, J_r and J_θ in the wave equations 2.35 and 2.38 gives

$$\frac{1}{r} \frac{\partial}{\partial r} \left(r \frac{\partial E_z}{\partial r} \right) - \gamma^2 E_z = 0 \qquad 2.48$$

and

$$\frac{1}{r} \frac{\partial}{\partial r} \left(r \frac{\partial H_z}{\partial r} \right) - \gamma^2 H_z = 0 \qquad 2.49$$

Consequently, we have two equations for E_z and H_z and the solutions are of the form $A' I_0(\gamma r) + B' K_0(\gamma r)$ where A' and B' are constants ($K_0(\gamma r)$ is omitted for inside the beam as before, Section 2.2.2.1).

Finally, boundary conditions are applied for the beam in a coaxial conducting cylinder of radius a by matching the 'E_0' wave admittances for inside and outside the beam, equating them at $r = b$.

The wave admittance for inside the beam is, by definition

$$\left(\frac{H_\theta + G_z}{E_z} \right) = Y_1$$

and for outside the beam it is

$$H_\theta / E_z = Y_2 .$$

Eqns 2.36, 2.41, 2.47 and 2.48 combined with $G_z = \rho_0 u_0 r_1$ give

$$Y_1 = \frac{j\omega\varepsilon_0}{\gamma} (1 - X) \frac{I_1(\gamma r)}{I_0(\gamma r)}$$

where
$$X = \frac{\omega_p^2}{(\omega - \gamma u_0)^2}.$$

For outside the beam let

$$E_z = B' I_0(\gamma r) + C' K_0(\gamma r) \qquad 2.50$$

and

$$H_\theta = \frac{j\omega\varepsilon_0}{\gamma} \left[B' I_1(\gamma r) - C' K_1(\gamma r) \right]. \qquad 2.51$$

Therefore,

$$Y_2 = \frac{j\omega\varepsilon_0}{\gamma} \left[\frac{I_1(\gamma r) - \left(\dfrac{C'}{B'}\right) K_1(\gamma r)}{I_0(\gamma r) + \left(\dfrac{C'}{B'}\right) K_0(\gamma r)} \right].$$

But $Y_1 = Y_2$ at $r = b$ and $E_z = 0$ at $r = a$

therefore
$$\frac{C'}{B'} = - \frac{I_0(\gamma a)}{K_0(\gamma a)}$$

and therefore

$$1 - \left\{ \frac{I_1(\gamma b) - \left[\dfrac{I_0(\gamma a)}{K_0(\gamma a)}\right] K_1(\gamma b)}{I_0(\gamma b) - \left[\dfrac{I_0(\gamma a)}{K_0(\gamma a)}\right] K_0(\gamma b)} \right\} \frac{I_0(\gamma b)}{I_1(\gamma b)} = X. \qquad 2.52$$

This enables one to plot $\sqrt{X}$ *versus* γb for various values of $1/R_1$ ($= b/a$). Those computed by Rigrod and Lewis [25] are shown in Figure 11. (The intrinsic solution is also shown, i.e. $\sqrt{X} = 1$.)

For space-charge waves we must have

$$\gamma_1 = \frac{\omega}{u_0} + \frac{\omega_p}{u_0 \sqrt{X'}}$$

and

$$\gamma_2 = \frac{\omega}{u_0} - \frac{\omega_p}{u_0 \sqrt{X''}}$$

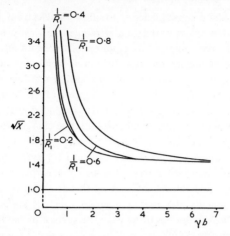

Figure 11. Plasma frequency reduction factors for a solid cylindrical electron beam in Brillouin flow, in a coaxial conducting cylinder

and we solve each of these equations with Eqn 2.52 to find the values of X' and X''.

If the wavelength of the standing wave created by these two space-charge waves $= \lambda_s$ we have

$$\lambda_s = \frac{4\pi}{(\gamma_1 - \gamma_2)}$$

and if $X' = X''$

$$\lambda_s \simeq \frac{2\pi u_0}{\omega_p} \sqrt{X}$$

therefore

$$\lambda_s \propto \sqrt{X} .$$

2.3.4. Discussion

The above analysis shows that there are several consequences of lowering the intensity of the longitudinal focusing field and shielding the cathode to give perfect Brillouin flow. (Magnetic shielding is discussed by Zworykin *et al.* [26]). We will consider each in turn, together with some other points of interest.

1. The immediate consequence is to allow the electrons in the beam to have a radial velocity and one is obliged to devise a method of simplifying the mathematics this 'rippling' of the beam introduces.

This is done by making the flow 'Brillouin', which gives a constant $\dot{\theta}_0$ (Section 2.3.1), and by assuming that we have a rectiliner beam which has an a.c. surface charge density, the interior of the beam having an unknown a.c. space-charge density. It is concluded that the rippling of the beam is accompanied by a constant space-charge density and not by space-charge bunching. This method was devised by Rigrod and Lewis [25] although Feenberg and Feldman [27] used a similar device in a 'kinematic' analysis. Labus [28] repeated an earlier criticism of this method [Labus and Pöschl, 29], saying that it neglected the effects of radial displacements and that it assumes that the surface charge is made up exclusively by electrons near the surface of the beam. Labus used a different system and obtained different results. It was subsequently shown that if applied correctly the two methods gave the same results [Rigrod and Labus, 30].

The possibility of a rippled beam producing gain is discussed in Section 3.2.4.

2. In addition to the other assumptions as set out in Section 2.2.1, which were considered to apply, it was assumed that the convection current density in the beam is the same order of magnitude as the displacement current density [Beck, 31]. This has, in fact, already been assumed in the analysis proving that the a.c. values of magnetic field can be ignored [Hutter, 11].

3. With the exception of the equation for G_θ

$$G_\theta = \rho_0 r_1 \dot{\theta}_0 b$$

the final wave equations and the ballistic equations are independent of B_{z0}, the applied longitudinal magnetic field. Thus, with the exception of this component of the surface current line-density, the same results apply to the case of zero longitudinal magnetic field.

4. Two pairs of space-charge waves appear to be present in this case,

(a) The intrinsic solution $\omega_p^2/(\omega - \gamma u_0)^2 = 1$ which is plotted in Figure 11, i.e. $\sqrt{X} = 1$ and

(b) The principal solution $\rho = 0$.

In both cases the space-charge waves are unattenuated. It may be, however, that some important points are lost as a result of the restrictions put on the analysis (Section 2.4).

5. By plotting $\sqrt{X}$ *versus* $(\gamma_0 b)$ for the Hahn-Ramo rectiliner flow pair of space-charge waves on the same axes, it is seen that since $\sqrt{(X)} \propto \lambda_s$,

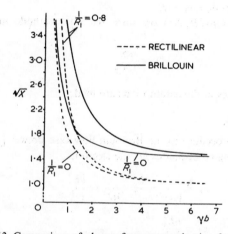

Figure 12. Comparison of plasma frequency reduction factors for a solid cylindrical electron beam in rectilinear flow and in Brillouin flow, in a coaxial conducting cylinder

the wavelength of the principal pair of waves in Brillouin flow is greater then the wavelength of the waves in rectiliner flow (Figure 12).

It must be admitted that the Brillouin flow condition is a very special case and one that is very difficult to achieve in practice. Nevertheless, it has served as a very useful introduction·to the more practical case we consider next.

2.4 PROPAGATION IN ARBITRARY LONGITUDINAL MAGNETIC FIELDS

2.4.1. Assumptions

In Section 2.3.1 we derived the expression $\dot{\theta}_0 = \omega_L(1-K)$ where $\omega_L = \eta(B_{z0}/2)$ and $K = r_c^2 B_c / r^2 B_{z0}$ and $\dot{\theta}_0$ is the angular velocity of the electrons in the beam. Also in Section 2.3.1 we discussed the special case of $K=0$, i.e. $B_c = 0$, no linking field at the cathode.

Now, we are concerned with cases where $K \neq 0$ and define a new parameter Ω where $\dot{\theta}_0 = \omega_L - \Omega$.

Thus $\Omega = \omega_L K = \eta(r_c^2 B_c / 2r^2)$ or, since the total cathode magnetic flux $\phi_c = \pi r_c^2 B_c$

$$\Omega = \frac{\eta \phi_c}{2r^2 \pi} \qquad 2.53$$

No other changes in the assumptions are made.

2.4.2. The analysis

By the identical procedure to the Brillouin flow case Brewer [32] obtained the following co-ordinates for the electrons:

$$r_1 = \frac{\eta E_r}{(\omega - \gamma u_0)^2 - 4\Omega^2} = \frac{\eta E_r}{\omega_0^2}$$

$$z_1 = \frac{\eta E_z}{\omega_b^2}$$

where $\omega_0^2 = \omega_b^2 - 4\Omega^2$ and $\omega_b^2 = (\omega - \gamma u_0)^2$.

The analysis is given in detail in Appendix 5.

Note that, if $B_c = \infty$ – the rectiliner flow case, we have $r_1 = 0$ and if $B_c = 0$ – the Brillouin flow case,

$$r_1 = \frac{\eta E_r}{(\omega - \gamma u_0)^2}$$

as before (Section 2.3.3).

Combining the wave equations with the expressions for the components of the convection current density and the a.c. charge density we obtain, for slow waves ($\gamma^2 \gg k^2$)

$$\frac{\partial^2 E_z}{\partial r^2} + \frac{1}{r}\frac{\partial E_z}{\partial r} - \gamma^2 \left[\frac{\dfrac{\omega_p^2}{\omega_b^2} - 1}{\dfrac{\omega_p^2}{\omega_0^2} - 1}\right] E_z = 0. \qquad 2.54$$

Putting

$$\tau_2^2 = \gamma^2 \left[\frac{\dfrac{\omega_p^2}{\omega_b^2} - 1}{\dfrac{\omega_p^2}{\omega_0^2} - 1}\right] \qquad 2.55$$

gives

$$\frac{1}{r}\frac{\partial}{\partial r}\left(r\frac{\partial E_z}{\partial r}\right) - \tau_2^2 E_z = 0 \qquad 2.56$$

which is the same form as Eqn 2.48 (p. 43) and has a solution of the form $A'I_0(\tau_2 r)$ inside the beam.

By letting

$$E_z = B'I_0(\gamma r) + C'K_0(\gamma r) \qquad (2.50)$$

and

$$H_\theta = \frac{j\omega\varepsilon_0}{\gamma}\left[B'I_1(\gamma r) - C'K_1(\gamma r)\right] \qquad (2.51)$$

for outside the beam as before, equating beam admittances at the beam boundary, $r=b$, gives

$$-\frac{\tau_2}{\gamma}\left[1 - \frac{\omega_p^2}{\omega_b^2}\right]\cdot\frac{I_1(\tau_2 b)}{I_0(\tau_2 b)} = \left[\frac{I_1(\gamma b) - \left(\dfrac{C'}{B'}\right)K_1(\gamma b)}{I_0(\gamma b) + \left(\dfrac{C'}{B'}\right)K_0(\gamma b)}\right] \qquad 2.57$$

and $C'/B' = -I_0(\gamma a)/K_0(\gamma a)$ since $E_z = 0$ at $r=a$.

Eqns 2.55 and 2.57 form two simultaneous equations for τ_2 and γ and as

$$\gamma = \gamma_0\left(1 \pm \frac{\omega_p}{u_0\sqrt{X}}\right)$$

we may find γ.

2.4.3. Plasma frequency reduction factors

Eqn 2.57 facilitates the determination of the plasma frequency reduction factor $\omega_b/\omega_p = p \; (= 1/\sqrt{X})$ in terms of Ω/ω_p, γb and R_1.

The curves computed by Brewer [32] are shown in Figures 13 to 20.

Figure 13 shows p *versus* (γb), with $1/R_1$ as parameter, for $\Omega/\omega_p = 0$. This is the Brillouin flow case and the author has demonstrated that if the curves of Figure 11 are transposed and plotted on the same axes as Figure 13, identical curves are obtained, as would be expected. Figures

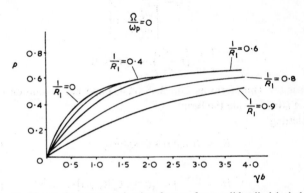

Figure 13. Plasma frequency reduction factors for a solid cylindrical electron beam in Brillouin flow, in a coaxial conducting cylinder

14 and 15 are plots of p *versus* γb, with $1/R_1$ as parameter, for $\Omega/\omega_p = 0.5$ and ∞ respectively. If we transpose the curve for $1/R_1 = 0.8$ of Figure 14 and plot on the same axes as Figure 12, we can see at a glance the effect of longitudinal magnetic field strength on the plasma frequency reduction factor (Figure 16). To consider the effect of the longitudinal magnetic field on a system with a particular geometry, we plot p *versus* (γb), with Ω/ω_p as parameter, for given values of $1/R_1$. Two examples (for $1/R_1 = 0.8$ and 0.4) are given in Figures 17 and 18. Also shown are curves of p *versus* Ω/ω_p, with γb as parameter, for two values of $1/R_1$ (Figures 19 and 20).

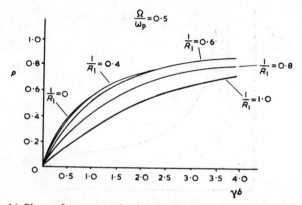

Figure 14. Plasma frequency reduction factors for a solid cylindrical electron beam in an arbitrary longitudinal magnetic focusing field, in a coaxial conducting cylinder

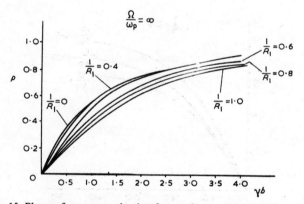

Figure 15. Plasma frequency reduction factors for a solid cylindrical electron beam in rectilinear flow, in a coaxial conducting cylinder

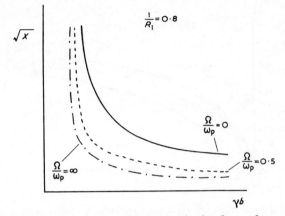

Figure 16. Comparison of plasma frequency reduction factors for an electron beam in various longitudinal magnetic field strengths, in a coaxial conducting cylinder

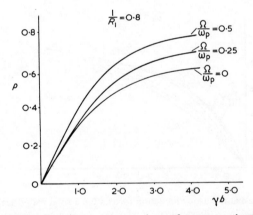

Figure 17. The effect of geometry on plasma frequency reduction factors

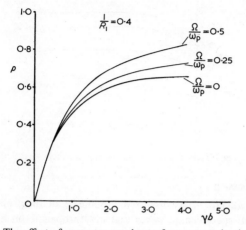

Figure 18. The effect of geometry on plasma frequency reduction factors

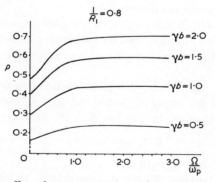

Figure 19. The effect of geometry on plasma frequency reduction factors

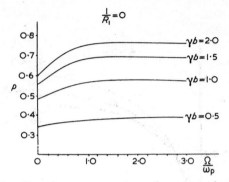

Figure 20. The effect of geometry on plasma frequency reduction factors

2.4.4. Discussion

In Section 2.2.5 (p. 34) we discussed, in some detail, the properties of the longitudinal space-charge waves that may propagate on moving electron beams in very high longitudinal magnetic fields. We are now concerned to know how these properties are affected by reducing the strength of the magnetic field, and most of the information required is found in the graphs just described.

Figures 19 and 20 indicate that there is little effect due to reducing the magnetic field strength until Ω/ω_p is approximately 2. This enables us to state what we mean by 'very high magnetic field strength' more precisely.

We can say that if $\Omega/\omega_p > 2$, then the electron flow is approximately rectiliner and the theory of Section 2.2 applies. Since $\Omega = \eta\phi_c/2\pi r^2$ [Eqn 2.53] and, in this case, $\phi_c = \pi r_c^2 B_c$

$$\Omega/\omega_p = \omega_L/\omega_p \quad \text{if } r = r_c$$

(where, in this case $\omega_L = \eta(B_c/2)$).

Thus the condition for the electron flow to be rectiliner is that $\omega_L/\omega_p > 2$ and the magnetic field strength is 'very high' if $\omega_L > 2\omega_p$ i.e. if $B_c > 4\omega_p/\eta$. This indicates that the longitudinal field strength required to produce a rectilinear beam is directly proportional to $\sqrt{\rho_0}$ the square root of the d.c. charge density of electrons in the beam.

The expression for the a.c. perturbation of electrons in the radial direction (Section 2.4.2) indicates that when $\Omega/\omega_p = 2$ the beam is still rippled. The ripples are so small that they do not produce a first order effect on the propagation characteristics of the system.

As Ω/ω_p is reduced below 2 so the fringing effects become significant. The lower the field strength becomes, so more of the electric flux passes to the outside of the beam, (Figure 21). Consequently the de-bunching forces, and thus the plasma frequency reduction factor p, are reduced; the overall picture is independent of R_1. For values of $\Omega/\omega_p > 1$, the effect of finite beam size (as expressed by γb) is greater than that of the proximity of the wall, but as Ω/ω_p is reduced below unity, so the effect

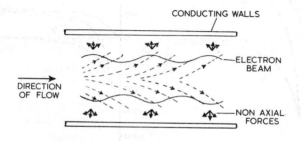

$-\ -\ -\ -$ ELECTRIC FLUX LINES

Figure 21. Illustration of how the de-bunching forces are reduced

of the proximity of the wall becomes increasingly significant. (Figures 13, 14, and 15.) The total variation in p from $\Omega = 0$ to $\Omega = \infty$ is about 40% for Ω/ω_p increasing from 2 to ∞ in the infinite beam. As the beam becomes finite in size this figure increases. The largest changes in p take place for Ω/ω_p varying between zero and 1·5.

We also conclude that:

When $\Omega = 0$ the electrons in the beam have radial and axial a.c. displacements but no a.c. rotation. In this type of motion the total axially directed electron flux into a small volume of the beam is just equal to the total radially directed electron flux out of the same volume. Consequently, there is no axial electron bunching. The axial velocity is unaffected.

When $0 < \Omega < \infty$ the electrons have a.c. rotations as well as radial and axial a.c. displacements. Therefore the radial electron velocity is affected, but the axial velocity is not. Consequently the unbalance results in the formation of electron bunching.

When $\Omega = \infty$ there is no longer a radial velocity and one obtains bunching in a smooth stream.

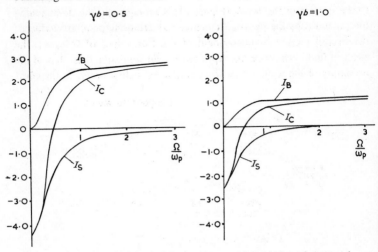

Figure 22. Variation of electron beam currents ($\gamma b = 0.5$)

Figure 23. Variation of electron beam currents ($\gamma b = 1.0$)

It is possible to compute the beam currents.

The total body convection current $I_{B(\text{tot})} = 2\pi \int_0^b r J_z \, dr$.

The total surface convection current $I_{S(\text{tot})} = 2\pi b G_z$.

Therefore the total convection current $I_{C(\text{tot})} = I_{B(\text{tot})} + I_{S(\text{tot})}$.

Using the values obtained for J_z and G_z we find

$$I_{B(\text{tot})} = j\omega\varepsilon_0 A' 2\pi b^2 I_1(\tau_2 b) \frac{[(4\Omega^2/\omega_p^2 + (1-p^2)]}{H p^2 \gamma b}$$

where

$$H = \left\{ \left(1 - p^2 + \frac{4\Omega^2}{\omega_p^2}\right)\left(\frac{1}{p^2} - 1\right)\left(p^2 - \frac{4\Omega^2}{\omega_p^2}\right) \right\}^{\frac{1}{2}}.$$

$I_{C(tot)}$ together with the constituent parts $I_{B(tot)}$ and $I_{S(tot)}$ are plotted in Figures 22 to 24. We see from these that for small values of Ω/ω_p the total convection current is made up primarily of the surface convection current, but as Ω/ω_p increases so the body convection current takes an increasingly large part of the total effect and at $\Omega/\omega_p \simeq 1\cdot 5$ the body convection current predominates. This is independent of γb.

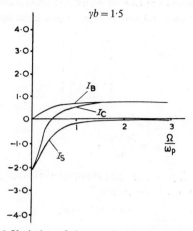

Figure 24. Variation of electron beam currents ($\gamma b = 1\cdot 5$)

Summarizing, the propagation of space-charge waves in a cylindrical electron beam moving in a longitudinal magnetic field, has been considered in three stages. Firstly, the case in which the longitudinal magnetic field strength was infinite was considered, and the a.c. charge density was found to be

$$\rho = -j\,\frac{\omega_p^2}{\omega_b^2}\,\varepsilon_0\,\gamma E_z$$

and the variation of E_z was expressed as a function of $J_0(Tr)$ where

$$T = \left\{ (k^2 - \gamma^2)\left(1 - \frac{\omega_p^2}{\omega_b^2} \right) \right\}^{\frac{1}{2}}.$$

Since $\gamma^2 \gg k^2$ and $\omega_p^2/\omega^2 < 1$, T is imaginary.

Secondly we considered the Brillouin flow case; we found that the a.c. charge density was zero and the variation of E_z was expressed as a function of $I_0(\gamma r)$ with a real radial propagation constant so that space-charge waves cannot propagate if the beam fills the drift-tube. If the beam does not fill the drift-tube space-charge waves can propagate. Finally, we discussed the case in which the longitudinal magnetic field strength was between the two extremes considered earlier. In this case we had

$$\tau_2^2 = \gamma^2 \frac{\left[\dfrac{\omega_p^2}{\omega_b^2} - 1\right]}{\left[\dfrac{\omega_p^2}{\omega_0^2} - 1\right]}$$

and

$$\rho = \frac{j\omega_p^2 \varepsilon_0 \gamma}{\omega_0^2} \left[\frac{\tau_2^2}{\gamma^2} - \frac{\omega_0^2}{\omega_b^2}\right] E_z .$$

Now if $\omega_0^2 = \omega_p^2$, $\gamma^2 = 0$, i.e. the propagation characteristics are divided up into two sections at the points

$$\omega_b^2 - 4\Omega^2 = \omega_p^2 .$$

2.4.5. The complete set of modes

In 1957 and 1958 Newton [33, 34, 35], published a series of papers. He pointed out that in a beam that is not in an infinite longitudinal magnetic field, there are four initial conditions to be satisfied (assuming the drift-tube does not propagate), namely, the three components of velocity and the charge density. One might expect, therefore, that four modes of propagation existed. It was shown that in addition to the two modes discussed in Section 2.4 there is, in the Brillouin flow case, a separate pair of modes associated with the cyclotron frequency. Newton criticized Rigrod and Lewis [30] (and therefore Brewer [32] by implication) on the grounds that they used the equation

$$\eta E_{r0} = (r_0 + r_1)\omega_L^2$$

where r_1 is the a.c. perturbation of r and E_{r0} is the unperturbed steady radial electric field, whereas a more suitable equation would be

$$\eta E_{r0} = r_0 \omega_L^2$$

and

$$E_r = E_{r0} + E_{r1}.$$

These give

$$r_1 = \eta E_{r1}/(\omega_b^2 - \omega_L^2)$$

instead of

$$r_1 = \eta E_{r1}/\omega_b^2.$$

The implication of this is discussed in Section 2.4.5.1.

This work started a slight controversy. Early in 1959, soon after the last of Newton's three papers was published, Trevena [36] criticized Newton because he failed to take into consideration the cathode magnetic flux. Trevena gave an analysis purporting to show that one could obtain the other set of modes referred to by Newton, for all values of cathode magnetic flux. Newton [37] quickly replied to the criticism that he had failed to take the cathode magnetic flux into consideration, and pointed out that Trevena's analysis holds only when Ω is independent of r, that it was because Ω depends on r that he, Newton, limited his analysis to the case when $\Omega = 0$. In any case, Trevena's Eqn 14

$$\tau^2 \left[1 - \frac{\omega_p^2}{(\omega_b^2 - 4\Omega^2)} \right] = \gamma^2 \left(1 - \frac{\omega_p^2}{\omega_b^2} \right)$$

is the same as that given by Brewer. It is interesting to note that so far as can be established, nobody has mentioned the fact that Brewer also assumed that Ω is independent of r (which is only true if $r_c = r$) and that this tends to invalidate part of Brewer's analysis. One should also treat with suspicion the curves given by Trevena for this reason.

Later in 1959, Paschke [38] published an analysis which also gave the additional set of modes associated with the cyclotron frequency and he criticized, in some detail, the work of Rigrod and Lewis and Brewer. He made no reference to the work of Newton in his paper, but added a note in proof. Although one cannot be certain, it would appear that Newton and Paschke were working independently and were unaware of each other's work. In one sense this is fortunate because, although the analyses and results appear to be very different, it can be shown that they in fact produce the same equations and one would be tempted to accept them, particularly as Newton [37] made use of Trevena's method to obtain the results of his previous paper.

This apparently happy situation was not to last long, because early in 1962 Kent [39] in the latest paper on this subject, came down firmly on the side of Rigrod and Lewis and against Newton and Paschke.

In order to summarize and simplify the extremely confusing situation, the author has produced an analysis which is a logical extension of the theory as developed to date. This combines the best features of the work of Newton, Paschke and Trevena and it is suggested that this rationalizes the situation and brings it up to date.

2.4.5.1. *The analysis*

The crux of the matter is that Rigrod and Lewis used the symbol E_r and it was understood to be the perturbation of the radial electric field at a constant radius of the beam. It assumes that when the electron moves from a position r_0 to $(r_0 + r_1)$ the field acting on it does not change. This may be nearly true, but one should not neglect the perturbed field without adequate evidence to the effect that it is a negligible quantity. Consequently E_r should be taken to be the perturbation of the electric field as seen by the electron during its displacement. It is for this reason that one should substitute $(E_{r0} + E_{r1})$ for E_r, where E_{r0} is the unperturbed steady state field at r_0 and E_{r1} is the perturbation on E_{r0}.

Since the analysis is very similar to the previous ones, only the essential parts are given: the assumptions are unchanged.

The continuity equation $\operatorname{div} \mathbf{J} + \dfrac{\partial \rho}{\partial t} = 0$

the Lorentz equation $\eta[\mathbf{E} + (\mathbf{u} \times \mathbf{B})] = d\mathbf{u}/dt$

and Maxwell's Equation $\operatorname{div} \mathbf{E} = \rho/\varepsilon_0$

are used together with $\dot{\theta}_0 = \omega_L - \Omega$ as before.

For the steady-state condition, we have from the Lorentz equation

$$\eta E_{r0} - \eta \dot{\theta}_0 r_0 B_{z0} = -\dot{\theta}_0^2 r_0$$

which gives $\eta E_{r0} - 2\omega_L r_0(\omega_L - \Omega) = -r_0(\omega_L - \Omega)^2$ 2.58

i.e. $\eta E_{r0} = r_0(\omega_L^2 - \Omega^2)$

Maxwell's equation gives

$$\eta E_{r0} = \frac{\omega_p^2}{2} r_0 \quad \text{(assuming } E_r = 0 \text{ at } r = 0)$$

and hence

$$\omega_p^2 + 2(\Omega^2 - \omega_L^2) = 0 .$$

When the beam is perturbed, put

$$r = r_0 + r_1 , \quad \theta = \theta_0 + \theta_1 , \quad E_r = E_{r0} + E_{r1} .$$

The Lorentz equation gives

$$\ddot{r} - r\dot{\theta}^2 = \eta E_r - 2\omega_L r\dot{\theta}$$

therefore

$$\ddot{r}_1 - (r_0 + r_1)(\dot{\theta}_0 + \dot{\theta}_1)^2 = \eta(E_{r0} + E_{r1}) - 2\omega_L(r_0 + r_1)(\dot{\theta}_0 + \dot{\theta}_1)$$

and this reduces to

$$\ddot{r}_1 + 2r_0\dot{\theta}_1\Omega + (\omega_L^2 - \Omega^2)r_1 = \eta E_{r1}. \qquad 2.59$$

The Lorentz equation also gives

$$r\ddot{\theta} + 2\dot{r}\dot{\theta} = 2\omega_L\dot{r}$$

and this becomes

$$r_0\dot{\theta}_1 - 2\Omega r_1 = 0 . \qquad 2.60$$

Finally 2.59 and 2.60 combine to give

$$\ddot{r}_1 + (\omega_L^2 + 3\Omega^2)r_1 = \eta E_{r1} \qquad 2.61$$

and so we obtain

$$r_1 = \frac{\eta E_{r1}}{(\omega_b^2 - 3\Omega^2 - \omega_L^2)} .$$

Now

$$\nabla . \bar{v} = -j\omega_b(\rho/\rho_0) \qquad (A3.16)$$

$$\frac{1}{r}\frac{\partial}{\partial r}(rv_r) - j\gamma v_z = -j\omega_b\frac{\rho}{\rho_0}$$

therefore

$$\frac{1}{r}\frac{\partial}{\partial r}\left(\frac{r\eta E_{r1}}{\omega_L^2 + 3\Omega^2 - \omega_b^2}\right) + \frac{\gamma}{\omega_b}v_z = +\frac{\rho}{\rho_0} . \qquad (A3.7)$$

Together with the equation $E_r = (j/\gamma)(\partial E_z/\partial r)$ the usual method is adopted to obtain equation

$$\frac{1}{r} \cdot \frac{\partial}{\partial r}\left(r \frac{\partial E_z}{\partial r}\right) - \tau_3^2 E_z = 0$$

where

$$\left\{1 + \frac{\omega_p^2}{\omega_L^2 + 3\Omega^2 - \omega_b^2}\right\} \tau_3^2 = \gamma^2 \left\{1 - \frac{\omega_p^2}{\omega_b^2}\right\} \qquad 2.62$$

assuming $\quad E_z = A' J_0(\tau_3 r)$.

But $\quad \Omega^2 = \omega_L^2 - (\omega_p^2/2)$

therefore $\quad \omega_L^2 + 3\Omega^2 = 4\omega_L^2 - \tfrac{3}{2}\omega_p^2$.

Put $\quad a^2 = \left\{\left(\frac{4\omega_L^2}{\omega_p^2}\right) - \tfrac{3}{2}\right\} = \left\{\left(\frac{\omega_c^2}{\omega_p^2}\right) - \tfrac{3}{2}\right\}$

therefore $\quad \omega_L^2 + 3\Omega^2 = a^2 \omega_p^2$.

Therefore we have

$$\left\{1 + \frac{\omega_p^2}{(a^2 \omega_p^2 - \omega_b^2)}\right\} \tau_3^2 = \gamma^2 \left\{1 - \frac{\omega_p^2}{\omega_b^2}\right\}.$$

But the plasma frequency reduction factor $p = \omega_b/\omega_p$

therefore

$$\left\{1 + \frac{1}{a^2 - p^2}\right\} \tau_3^2 = \gamma^2 \left\{1 - \frac{1}{p^2}\right\}$$

therefore

$$\left\{\frac{a^2 + 1 - p^2}{a^2 - p^2}\right\} \tau_3^2 = \gamma^2 \frac{(p^2 - 1)}{p^2}.$$

This is an expression for the plasma frequency reduction factor and gives

$$p^2 = \frac{(1 + a^2)}{2}\left\{1 \pm \left[1 - \frac{4a^2}{(1 + a^2)^2\left(1 - \frac{\tau_3^2}{\gamma^2}\right)}\right]^{\frac{1}{2}}\right\} \qquad 2.63$$

In exactly the same way as in the earlier analysis, there are an infinite number of solutions to the transcendental equation and Eqn 2.63 applies for all such solutions.

Typical curves of $|p|$ *versus* γb for differing values of a^2 were given by Paschke [38] and are shown in Figures 25 to 27. These are for the zero

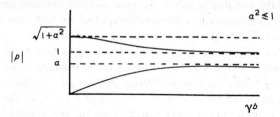

Fig. 25. Illustration of the four modes of propagation of space-charge waves when $a^2 \leqslant 1$

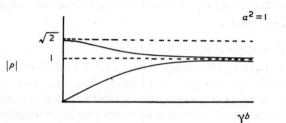

Figure 26. Illustration of the four modes of propagation of space-charge waves when $a^2 = 1$

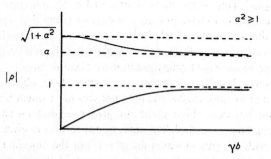

Figure 27. Illustration of the four modes of propagation of space-charge waves when $a^2 \geqslant 1$

order waves. They indicate that in addition to the pair of waves obtained earlier in which $|p| < 1$, there is another pair in which $|p| > 1$. The form of the first pair is exactly the same as those obtained earlier and the dispersion equation is the same except that we now have the term a^2 instead of $(2\Omega/\omega_p)^2$.

The two pairs of waves can be considered by looking at the limit of $|p|$ for large γb. For $\frac{1}{2} \leqslant a^2 \leqslant 1$ where $\frac{1}{2}$ is the Brillouin value (since if $\Omega = 0$, $4\omega_L^2 = 2\omega_p^2$) the effective plasma frequency of the lower branch $\rightarrow a\omega_p$ and of the upper branch it $\rightarrow \omega_p$. For $1 \leqslant a^2 \leqslant \infty$ the effective plasma frequency of the upper branch $\rightarrow a\omega_p$ and of the lower branch it $\rightarrow \omega_p$, which is the radial eigenfrequency of the electrons [Eqn 2.61]. Thus each can be said to be associated with one of the two possible resonance frequencies of the system; the radial frequency $a\omega_p$ or the plasma frequency ω_p.

2.4.5.2. Comparison of the two sets of results

The Rigrod and Lewis analysis indicated for the first time that there might possibly be two pairs of waves. It shows that there was an 'intrinsic' pair of waves with propagation constants equal to those of the waves propagating on a stream in rectilinear flow, and a 'principal' pair for which the space-charge density ρ was zero. Unfortunately, the 'intrinsic' pair of waves lead to inconsistencies [Beck, 31] and had to be abandoned. Also Eqn 2.50 shows that if the beam fills the tube no waves can propagate. This seems to be unreasonable because one would expect a thick beam to have propagation characteristics that were very similar to that of a beam of infinite extent. Also, if the beam fills the tube, there can be no rippling, and one might ask if the two 'rectilinear' space-charge waves would propagate in these circumstances.

The complete analysis, however, overcomes these objections. It shows the four possible modes and does not give inconsistent results in the Brillouin flow case. This analysis also gives a solution for all values of longitudinal magnetic field. The analysis due to Brewer gives results consistent with the pair of waves for $|p| < 1$, but the objection to the Brewer analysis, apart from the fact that he too only used E_r instead of $(E_{r0} + E_{r1})$, is the fact that he assumed that Ω was independent of r

when substituting $(j/\gamma)(\partial E_z/\partial r)$ for E_r. If the cathode flux is constant this is approximately true for very thin beams, otherwise it is only true if $r_c = r$, a condition that holds only at one part of the beam. The complete analysis has the term $(\omega_L^2 + 3\Omega^2)$, compared with $4\Omega^2$, and this is independent of r thus overcoming this objection.

To sum up the position, therefore, we can say that if an electron beam moves in an infinite longitudinal magnetic field two space-charge waves propagate if excited. These waves are associated with the plasma frequency ω_p which is reduced by the fringing effects unless the beam is infinite in extent. If the longitudinal magnetic field strength is reduced to such an extent that $B_c < 4\omega_p/\eta$, then four space-charge waves propagate if they are excited. In addition to the pair of waves associated with the plasma frequency, there is a pair of waves associated with the cyclotron frequency. These have a reduction factor which is greater than unity.

2.5 FINAL COMMENTS

2.5.1. Applications of longitudinal space-charge-wave theory

The applications of longitudinal space-charge-wave-theory are numerous. Indeed, the action of nearly all microwave devices using electron beams can be explained in terms of the theory. However, the explanation of the operation of the majority of these devices involves rather more than the simple unattenuated space-charge waves. The problem of the interaction between the electron beam that supports these waves and a circuit is often involved. The travelling-wave tube [Pierce, 40] is an example of such a device. In this case the moving electron beam interacts with a slow wave structure.

The klystron is an example of a device the operation of which can be described in terms of a simple space-charge-wave theory. Briefly, the klystron consists of two resonators (or cavities). The first (the buncher) supplies an input signal to the moving electron beam passing through it. The signal excites both the fast and the slow space-charge waves in such a way that they are of equal magnitude and phased so that the velocity modulations add, but the convection current modulations cancel out. In other words, at the buncher there is velocity modulation but no convection current modulation. The second resonator (the catcher) is placed where the velocity modulations cancel out but where the convection current modulations add. This convection current modulation produces a voltage across the catcher, and energy is extracted from the beam. (The voltage across the catcher excites new slow and fast waves, such that the incident fast wave is reduced and the incident slow wave is increased on leaving the catcher).

As there is a vast amount of literature on both these devices, and each requires and merits a large amount of space, it is not proposed to discuss them further. In Chapter 3 we deal with the theory of some other devices.

2.5.2. Experimental work

Very little experimental work has been carried out with the sole view of investigating the space-charge-wave theory. With the more pressing and more mundane problem of the era from 1939, namely that of pro-

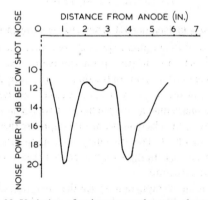

Figure 28. Variation of noise power along an electron beam

ducing practical, powerful devices, nearly all experimental work has been devoted to that end and the verification of the space-charge-wave theory has been purely incidental.

In an experimental investigation of noise in electron beams, Cutler and Quate [41] devised an experiment to measure the noise-power coupled from an electron beam into a resonant cavity which could be moved along the electron beam. Working at 4,200 Mc/s with a beam diameter of 0·050" (minimum) and a cathode current density of 40 mA/cm² they obtained the curves of Figure 28. These indicate that there are maxima and minima in the noise power obtained which would be expected if noise phenomena are visualized in terms of the two space-charge waves being excited by the noise. D. A. Watkins [17] also produced an experimental tube verifying this.

Other experimental work of interest is most likely to be found in studies of electron beam optics and the formation of electron beams, subjects that are not discussed in this monograph. Suffice it to say that according to Paschke [38], the experimental work of Berghammer [42], Schnitger [43], Lawson [44], and Schumann [45], gives good agreement with this theory.

CHAPTER 3

Increasing Space Charge Waves

3.1 GENERAL REMARKS

Soon after the postulation of the space-charge-wave theory by Hahn and Ramo, many workers commenced efforts to apply it to the devices then operating and also to see if it would lead to the invention of new devices.

Since one of the most useful types of device is the amplifier, one naturally looks for a mechanism that gives, in 'wave' terms, a negative attenuation constant, i.e. an increasing wave. We are, of course, concerned with waves that increase in space (sometimes called 'growing' waves) as opposed to waves that increase in time. Note that the klystron is not an increasing space-charge wave device. Its operation can be explained in terms of the beating of the simple unattenuated space-charge waves only.

This chapter, therefore, is devoted to a study of increasing space-charge waves and some of the devices that depend on such waves for their operation.

3.2 INCREASING SPACE-CHARGE WAVES ON SINGLE ELECTRON BEAMS

A variety of mechanisms for producing increasing space-charge waves on single electron beams have been proposed. A considerable amount of theoretical and experimental work has been carried out and this is discussed in the following sections.

3.2.1. Increasing space-charge waves on accelerated or retarded electron beams

In a historical letter, Field, Tien and Watkins [46] announced that they had found that if the velocity of a single electron beam changes, the space-charge waves not only change in wavelength, but also change in amplitude. By a suitable combination of gradual decelerations and sudden accelerations, the space-charge waves may increase without the aid of external wave carrying circuits or additional beams.

The fundamental theory was published by Tien and Field [47] in a later paper which also gave details of the various structures they had produced.

3.2.1.1. *Assumptions*

The assumptions are very similar to those used in the development of the space-charge-wave theory, but they are set out below for convenience:

(a) A.C. values are very small compared with d.c. values.
(b) There is a steady longitudinal d.c. magnetic field, of infinite strength, parallel to the direction of motion of the electron beam.
(c) There is a sufficient number of positive ions present to neutralize the d.c. effects of space-charge.
(d) Positive ions are assumed to have infinite mass so that they have no a.c. motion.
(e) The velocity of electrons is very much less than the velocity of light.
(f) Electrons are assumed to leave the cathode with zero d.c. velocity.

Thus the theory is reduced to a small-signal, one dimensional analysis. This gives nearly all the important information for a stream of small diameter. The ideal case of a beam of infinite extent has effectively the same d.c. conditions as the real small diameter beam. The a.c. effect of finite beam size is taken into account by the plasma frequency reduction factor.

3.2.1.2. *The space-charge wave matrix*

Since the problem has been reduced to a one-dimensional case, the total a.c. current of the stream (the a.c. convection current plus the a.c. displacement current) is zero [Hutter, 11]. Therefore the Llewellyn-Peterson [48] equations may be expressed as

$$J(z) = [E^* J(s) + F^* v(s)]\, e^{-d}\, e^{j\omega t}$$
$$v(z) = [H^* J(s) + I^* v(s)]\, e^{-d}\, e^{j\omega t}$$

where $J(z)$ = a.c. convection current density at the z plane

$v(z)$ = a.c. electron velocity at the z plane

$d = j\omega\tau_0$

τ_0 = d.c. transit time between the z plane and the starting plane s.

E^*, F^*, H^* and I^* are the Llewellyn coefficients and are functions of d.c. voltages and d.c. current densities at both ends of the space under consideration. E^* and I^* are dimensionless, F^* is conductance per unit area and H^* is resistance per unit area.

In a similar way, the space-charge waves on a stream may be expressed in the form

$$J(z) = [EJ(s) + Fv(s)]\, e^{-d}\, e^{j\omega t}$$
$$v(z) = [HJ(s) + Iv(s)]\, e^{-d}\, e^{j\omega t} \tag{3.1}$$

Here E, F, H and I are called space-charge wave coefficients and they are functions of the d.c. potential distribution in the space, in addition to the d.c. end conditions.

We should note that $d = j\omega\tau_0$ and for constant axial velocity $z = u_0\tau_0$, therefore $d = j\omega(z/u_0)$. The term $\exp(-d)\exp(j\omega t)$ shows the travelling wave of the perturbation frequency and the space-charge wave coefficients describe the variation in amplitude of the waves.

In matrix form Eqns 3.1 may be written

$$\left\| \begin{array}{c} J(z) \\ v(z) \end{array} \right\| = \left\| \begin{array}{cc} E & F \\ H & I \end{array} \right\| e^{-d}\, e^{j\omega t} \left\| \begin{array}{c} J(s) \\ v(s) \end{array} \right\|.$$

A more detailed discussion of the equivalence of Llewellyn and space-charge wave equations is given by Birdsall [49].

3.2.1.3. *Theory of space-charge waves in an infinite accelerated electron beam*

The accelerating space is divided into a large number of small sections; each section is treated as a separate diode and the Llewellyn equations are applied to each section. Figure 29 shows the system considered.

Between the starting plane (s) and the exit plane (e) there is a constant potential gradient dV_0/dz the potential being as shown. We assume the electron enters the accelerating space at the (s) plane. Define a positive quantity $x=(4\eta nez^{\frac{1}{2}}/\varepsilon_0 K^3)^2$, which is dimensionless, where $K=u_0z^{-\frac{1}{2}}$.

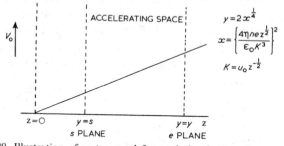

Figure 29. Illustration of system used for analysis of space-charge waves in accelerated beams

Figures 30 and 31 show the space-charge wave coefficients as functions of x. The coefficients are obtained from the Llewellyn coefficients after

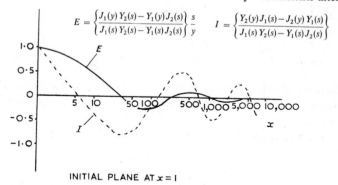

$$E = \left\{\frac{J_1(y)Y_2(s)-Y_1(y)J_2(s)}{J_1(s)Y_2(s)-Y_1(s)J_2(s)}\right\}\frac{s}{y} \qquad I = \left\{\frac{Y_2(y)J_1(s)-J_2(y)Y_1(s)}{J_1(s)Y_2(s)-Y_1(s)J_2(s)}\right\}$$

INITIAL PLANE AT $x=1$

Figure 30. The variation of the space-charge wave coefficients E and I

elimination of the space-charge wave factor [see Llewellyn and Peterson, 48] and are given on Figures 30 and 31.

The space-charge wave matrix with the initial plane at any other position, say $x=a$, is given by

$$\begin{Vmatrix} E_{ax} & F_{ax} \\ H_{ax} & I_{ax} \end{Vmatrix} = \begin{Vmatrix} E_{1a} & F_{1a} \\ H_{1a} & I_{1a} \end{Vmatrix}^{-1} \times \begin{Vmatrix} E_{1x} & F_{1x} \\ H_{1x} & I_{1x} \end{Vmatrix}$$

The first subscript denotes the position of the initial plane and the second subscript denotes the position of the plane under consideration, i.e. E_{1x}, F_{1x} etc. can be obtained from the curves with initial plane at $x = 1$. Figures 30 and 31 show that the space-charge wave coefficients

$$H = \left\{ \frac{J_2(y) Y_2(s) - Y_2(y) J_2(s)}{J_1(s) Y_2(s) - Y_1(s) J_2(s)} \frac{j \cdot s}{2G} \right\} \qquad F = \left\{ \frac{J_1(y) Y_1(s) - Y_1(y) J_1(s)}{J_1(s) Y_2(s) - Y_1(s) J_2(s)} \frac{j \cdot 2G}{y} \right\}$$

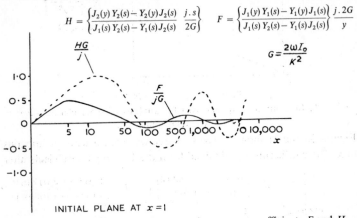

$$G = \frac{2\omega I_0}{K^2}$$

INITIAL PLANE AT $x = 1$

Figure 31. The variation of the space-charge wave coefficients F and H

have an oscillatory form with amplitude decreasing as x increases. Thus in an accelerated stream, the amplitude of the space-charge waves decreases.

For a retarded beam one uses the relationship

$$\begin{Vmatrix} E' & F' \\ H' & I' \end{Vmatrix} = \begin{Vmatrix} E & F \\ H & I \end{Vmatrix}^{-1}$$

and this is used to obtain curves for E', F', I' and H' – the space-charge wave coefficients for the retarded beam. Figures 32 and 33 show these coefficients for the initial plane at $x = 1000$ (Figures 34 and 35 show E and E' for other starting planes) and it is seen that the space-charge-wave amplitudes increase.

One might point out in passing that an accelerating field might possibly be used to reduce the noise content in an electron beam. Pierce [15] described an electron gun where the component of space-charge waves associated with noise current is de-amplified, by arranging

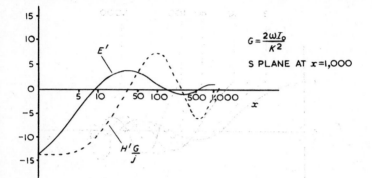

Figure 32. The variation of the space-charge wave coefficients E' and H'

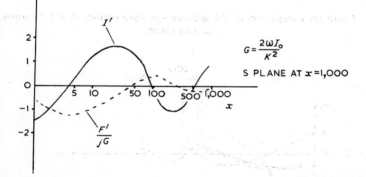

Figure 33. The variation of the space-charge wave coefficients F' and I'

to set up only the decreasing wave. There is a limit of 6 dB reduction of noise in this case. Watkins [17] also verified this figure experimentally in some low noise travelling-wave tubes and Peter [50] discussed this subject at some length.

An alternative analysis was referred to by Tien and Field in their classical paper and they indicated that Smullin was its originator. Smullin [51] later published his theory which is an electronic theory similar to that referred to in Section 2.2.3 (and given in Appendix 2).

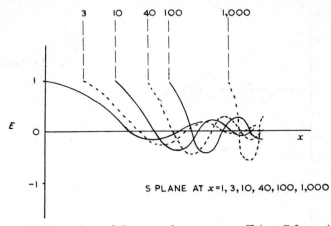

Figure 34. Comparison of the space-charge wave coefficient E for various starting planes

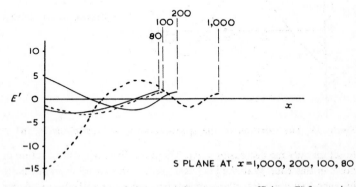

Figure 35. Comparison of the space-charge wave coefficient E' for various starting planes

3.2.1.4. *Amplifying structures*

The fact that increasing space-charge waves are obtained in a retarded electron beam suggests the possibility that one might be able to produce practical amplifying devices for signals of microwave frequencies. The graphs in Figure 36 show that, if an electron beam is perturbed in such a

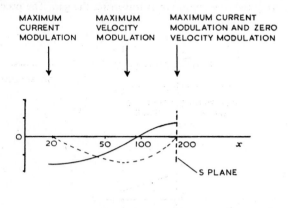

Figure 36. Illustration of how amplification may be obtained from a 'velocity-jump' system

way that it has maximum conduction current modulation and zero velocity modulation at $x = 200$, the conduction current modulation increases by a factor of about 3 at $x = 20$.

One possible amplifying structure using this fact is shown in Figure 37a. It consists of identical cylindrical sections, with alternate sections connected to a source of high potential and the other sections connected to a source of low potential. As seen in the diagram, the spaces between sections are alternately large and small, thus forming a retarding space and a short accelerating gap. The length of the retarding space is such that, if the electron beam enters the space with maximum current modulation it arrives at the other end also with maximum current modulation, i.e. it moves from the position where $x = 200$ to that where $x = 20$. The beam then receives a sudden jump from the low voltage back to the high voltage as it traverses the accelerating gap. This gap, sometimes called the 'voltage-jump gap' is very short compared with one-quarter of the space-charge wavelength, so that the current modulation changes very little during the time the beam is traversing the gap. The process

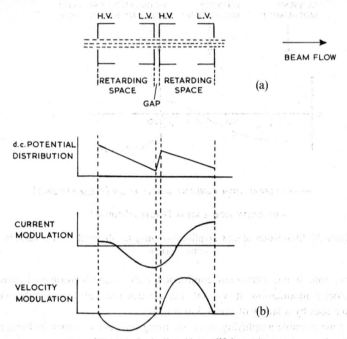

Figure 37. A 'velocity-jump' amplifying structure

can be repeated as the beam passes through each retarding space. Curves of the current modulation, velocity modulation and d.c. potential distribution are shown in Figure 37b.

The structure shown in Figure 38a produces a different d.c. potential distribution. In this case the high voltage drift-spaces are much longer than before, and the retarding spaces are much shorter than before. The lower voltage drift-spaces are unaltered, and the accelerating gaps are still very short compared with one-quarter of the space-charge wavelength. The d.c. potential distribution obtained, and the current and

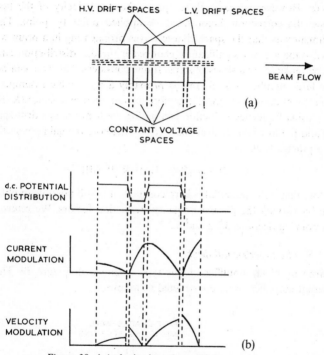

Figure 38. A 'velocity-jump' amplifying structure

velocity modulations are shown in Figure 38b. The gain per section, G, of this device is given by [Harman, 24]

$$G = 20 \log_{10} (V_{01}/V_{02})^{\frac{3}{4}} \text{ dB}$$

where V_{01} and V_{02} are the potentials of the high and low voltage sections respectively. So far, we have ignored the plasma frequency reduction factor that must be applied to take account of the finite size of the beam and the coaxial conducting cylinders surrounding the beam (Section 2.2.4). Tien and Field stated that the reduction factor that can be applied to the drift-spaces can also be applied to the retarding and accelerating spaces. However, since in these spaces the d.c. velocity of the beam varies, the correction factor must be applied point by point. Their argument was that the space-charge waves propagating in a beam with a drift-tube are not significantly changed if the d.c. distribution curve can be replaced by a series of steps. If one considers that there can be a very large number of steps this is probably a reasonable assumption. The expression for gain must, therefore, be modified by a factor (R'/R''), the plasma frequency reduction factors for the high voltage drift-space (R') and the low voltage drift-space (R''). Therefore the gain per section for a practical tube is

$$G = 20 \log_{10}[(V_{01}/V_{02})^{\frac{3}{4}}(R'/R'')]\mathrm{dB} \ .$$

Note that if the potential is kept constant, it is still possible to obtain gain by varying the plasma frequency reduction factors. We return to this point in Sections 3.2.2 and 3.2.3.

3.2.1.5. *The experimental devices*

A drawing of an amplifier of this type is shown in Figure 39. Three different amplifiers were constructed as follows:

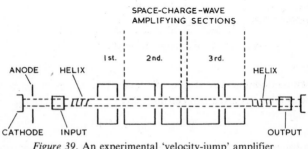

Figure 39. An experimental 'velocity-jump' amplifier

(1) An amplifier containing six cylindrical sections with the first three cylinders connected to the same potential and with the second three cylinders all connected to a lower potential. These form, therefore, in effect a single section space-charge-wave amplifying device. The retardation was from 1900 V to 65 V. With a beam of 0·055" diameter and a beam current of 0·6 mA, a gain of 24 dB was obtained at 3,000 Mc/s over and above that obtained when operated without the retardation.

(2) A two-cylinder amplifier with one long and one short cylinder. When operated with a retardation of from 860 V to 70 V, a 10 dB gain was obtained: all other parameters were as in (1) above.

(3) A three-cylinder amplifier with one cylinder 5·10 cm long and two cylinders 0·86 cm long. This was operated as a two-section space-charge-wave amplifying device with the input helix, at a potential of 680 V, being used as one element of the first section. The first retardation, from helix to first cylinder, was from 680 V to 66 V, and the second was from 500 V to 68 V. The second amplifying section produced a gain of 20 dB at 2891 Mc/s with a beam current of 0·50 mA. The total gain, including that obtained between the input helix and the first cylinder was 29 dB – all other operating conditions being as for the other two tubes.

3.2.1.6. *Discussion*

If it would work successfully, an amplifier of this type would have some advantages over the klystron and the travelling-wave tube.

It does not require a complicated circuit structure as in the travelling-wave tube and its gain is not so frequency dependent as in the klystron. It is not independent of frequency however as R is frequency dependent to a certain extent and there may well be other factors affecting the frequency response. This type of tube also possesses none of the problems of mixing of beams that are found in double-beam devices (Section 3.3).

The amplification obtained in these first practical devices ever produced was quite good and one would have expected further experiments to have been undertaken. Why then has very little else been reported? The answer to this question may be the fact that it was found that such devices required the use of a helix or cavity to modulate and de-modulate the beam (Figure 39). If a helix is to be used at all, one might as well use the same helix extended over the whole length of the device and have the additional advantages (particularly the wide frequency response) of the travelling-wave tube. Nevertheless, this was a fundamental step forward in the development of microwave devices and additional support for the space-charge-wave theory. Other similar devices were produced later, all of which are loosely described as space-charge-wave amplifiers. This particular amplifier is sometimes called, for obvious reasons, the velocity-jump amplifier.

Having found that amplification can be obtained by passing an electron beam through a drift-tube and applying a periodic change in potential, it is natural to enquire if a similar effect can be obtained by producing similar changes in field. Birdsall [52] considered the pendulum. If it swings downwards in a strong field, the amplitude of the swing will increase. Alternatively, if the pendulum's length or mass is increased during the swing downwards (or decreased during the swing upwards), then the amplitude of the swing will also increase. In the electronic analogy, if the electrons in a beam could be made to receive an alternating restoring force, say a potential jump, then the amplitude of their oscillations should increase. Similarly a change in field would also produce an increase in the amplitude of oscillations.

We see in Sections 3.2.3 and 3.2.4 that it is possible to produce such changes in field in two ways: firstly, by causing the electron beam to pass close to a conducting wall and then further away from it, so that the induced charges on the wall decrease and increase alternately, thus varying the de-bunching forces. Secondly, changes in field can be produced by altering the diameter of the beam. Here the beam has a larger de-bunching effect when it is smaller (higher current density) than when it is larger. Before discussing these methods further, an interesting analogy is investigated.

3.2.2. The transmission-line analogy

3.2.2.1. *The theory*

A small-signal analysis is made and the usual assumptions are applied to the rectilinear flow case.

The force equation gives

$$\frac{dv}{dt} = -\eta E = \frac{\partial v}{\partial t} + u_0 \frac{\partial v}{\partial z}.$$

Since

$$J + j\omega\varepsilon_0 E = 0$$

and

$$J = \rho_0 v + \rho u_0$$

we have

$$-\frac{\eta j J}{\omega\varepsilon_0} = \frac{\partial v}{\partial t} + u_0 \frac{\partial v}{\partial z} \qquad 3.2$$

and the continuity equation gives

$$u_0 \frac{\partial J}{\partial z} = -j\omega J + j\omega\rho_0 v. \qquad 3.3$$

Now introduce an a.c. potential V defined by the equation

$$2\eta(V_0 + V) = (u_0 + v)^2 \simeq u_0^2 + 2u_0 v$$

where V_0 is the d.c. potential of the beam: thus $u_0^2 = 2\eta V_0$ and $V = u_0 v/\eta$, therefore Eqns 3.2 and 3.3 become

$$dV/dz = (-j/\omega\varepsilon_0)J$$

and

$$dJ/dz = (j\omega J_0/2u_0 V_0) V.$$

If the cross-sectional area of the beam is A'' and I is the total current, $A'' J = I$

therefore

$$dV/dz = (-j/\omega\varepsilon_0 A'')I \qquad 3.4$$

and

$$dI/dz = (j\omega I_0/2u_0 V_0) V. \qquad 3.5$$

Now Eqns 3.4 and 3.5 are of the same form as the equations that describe a lossless transmission line, i.e.

$$dV/dz = jX_R I \qquad 3.6$$

and

$$dI/dz = jB_S V \qquad 3.7$$

and so it is possible to give to the beam a series reactance and a shunt susceptance per unit length.

Comparing Eqn 3.4 with 3.6 and Eqn 3.5 with 3.7 shows that

$$X_R = -1/(\omega \varepsilon_0 A'')$$

and

$$B_S = \omega I_0/(2u_0 V_0)$$

and these become

$$X_R = \frac{2V_0}{I_0} \cdot \frac{\omega}{u_0} \cdot \frac{\omega_p^2}{\omega^2}$$

and

$$B_S = -\frac{\omega A'' \varepsilon_0}{u_0^2} \omega_p^2$$

At this stage, two new parameters are introduced. They are: the phase constant

$$P_c = \sqrt{(X_R B_S)} \quad \left[=(-\omega I_0/2u_0 V_0 \omega \varepsilon_0 A'')^{\frac{1}{2}} = \omega_p/u_0 = \beta\right]$$

and the characteristic impedance

$$Z = \sqrt{(X_R/B_S)} \quad \left[= j(\omega_p/\omega)(2V_0/I_0)\right].$$

If we define the independant variable $v = \int_0^z P_c \, dz$
Eqn 3.6 gives

$$\frac{dV}{dv} = \frac{dV}{dz}\frac{dz}{dv} = \frac{1}{P_c}\frac{dV}{dz} = \frac{jX_R I}{P_c} = jZI$$

i.e.

$$\frac{dV}{dv} = jZI \qquad 3.8$$

and Eqn 3.7 gives

$$\frac{dI}{dv} = j\frac{V}{Z} = jZ^{-1}V. \qquad 3.9$$

For a practical tube the reduced plasma frequency must be used. The transmission-line analogue of the electron beam is shown in Figure 40.

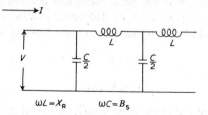

Figure 40. The transmission-line analogue of an electron beam

3.2.2.2. *Application to space-charge-wave amplifiers*

Consider a space-charge wave on a beam drifting at d.c. velocity u_0 with a.c. velocity v and a.c. convection current J in a stream in which the total d.c. current is I_0. Let the d.c. potential be V_0 and the a.c. potential be V. If the beam traverses a plane n, normal to the beam, and the a.c. current and a.c. voltage at this plane are I_n and V_n respectively, then at a

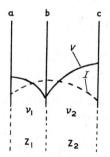

Figure 41. Application of the transmission-line analogue of an electron beam to space-charge-wave amplifiers

plane $n+1$, the a.c. current and a.c. voltage are I_{n+1} and V_{n+1} which are obtained from Eqns 3.9 and 3.8 respectively:

$$I_{n+1} = jZ^{-1} V_n \sin v + I_n \cos v \qquad 3.10$$

$$V_{n+1} = V_n \cos v + jZI_n \sin v \qquad 3.11$$

where $Z = \sqrt{(X_R/B_S)}$ as before (Section 3.2.2.1) and v now $= (\omega_p/u_0)z$.

Consider the system shown in Figure 41. This consists of three parallel planes a, b, c. The beam impedance between planes a and b is Z_1, and between b and c it is Z_2. Taking the current zero to be at plane a, as shown, at plane b we have from Eqns 3.10 and 3.11

$$I_b = j(V_a/Z_1) \sin v_1$$

and

$$V_b = V_a \cos v_1$$

If plane b is placed at the point where the potential is zero, i.e. $V_b = 0$, $v_1 = \pi/2$ and therefore

$$I_b = j(V_a/Z_1) .$$

Since at plane b the beam impedance Z_1 is changed to Z_2 it follows that

$$V_c = -(Z_2/Z_1) V_a \sin v_2$$

and

$$I_c = j(V_a/Z_1) \cos v_2$$

and if

$$V_2 = \frac{\pi}{2}$$

$$V_c = -(Z_2/Z_1) V_a$$
$$I_c = 0 .$$

(It would be more correct to consider current and potential minima. The assumption that these minima are zeros was made to simplify this example.)

The cycle is repeated if at plane c the impedance 'jumps' to the first beam impedance Z_1 and theoretically it can be repeated any number of times. In the system shown in Figure 41, the double impedance jump, we have

$$V_c/V_a = -Z_2/Z_1$$

i.e.

$$\left| \frac{V_c}{V_a} \right| = \frac{Z_2}{Z_1} .$$

Since $\qquad \omega_p = \sqrt{(-\eta\rho_0/\varepsilon_0)} \qquad \omega_p = \dfrac{j}{b}\sqrt{\left/\left(\dfrac{\eta I_0}{\pi\varepsilon_0 u_0}\right)\right.}$.

In the expression for Z we have to modify the plasma frequency to take into account the effect of geometry, i.e.

$$Z = j\,\frac{p\omega_p}{\omega}\cdot\frac{2V_0}{I_0}$$

and together with the equation $u_0^2 = 2\eta V_0$ it is found that

$$\left|\frac{V_c}{V_a}\right| = \left(\frac{V_{02}}{V_{01}}\right)^{\frac{3}{4}}\cdot\left(\frac{p_2}{p_1}\right)\cdot\left(\frac{b_1}{b_2}\right). \qquad\qquad 3.12$$

3.2.2.3. Discussion

The theory given in Section 3.2.2.1 was first given by Bloom and Peter [53] after a suggestion by Chu [54] that, since the space-charge-wave matrix is similar in form to the matrix of wave propagation on a uniform transmission line, one could make the two matrices identical if an a.c. potential were substituted for the a.c. velocity component in the beam. It shows that the differential equations describing the amplitude of the space-charge waves, on a beam in which all motion is confined to the z direction, are identical to those describing the e.m. wave propagation on a transmission line. This means that wave propagation on such beams may be studied by considering the equivalent transmission line, and such terms as series reactance and shunt susceptance can be applied to the electron beam. It is possible, therefore, to construct a transmission-line model of a particular electron beam, given such parameters as d.c. voltage, d.c. current and beam diameter, and to measure the standing wave along the line which represents the amplitude pattern of the space-charge waves. Bloom and Peter applied this to the planar diode and constructed a coaxial transmission-line model. The measured standing wave patterns agreed well with the calculated standing wave pattern.

The application of the transmission-line analogy to space-charge-wave amplifiers was performed by Peter, Bloom and Ruetz [55]. This shows that the velocity-jump amplifier (Section 3.2.1) is only a special case of the group of three amplifiers all of which operate by a change of beam impedance. Eqn 3.12 indicates that if the beam radius is kept constant

$$\left| \frac{V_c}{V_a} \right| = \left[\frac{V_{02}}{V_{01}} \right]^{\frac{3}{4}} \cdot \left[\frac{p_2}{p_1} \right]$$

which is the device described by Field, Tien and Watkins [46]. If however, V_0 and b are kept constant

$$\left| \frac{V_c}{V_a} \right| = \left[\frac{p_2}{p_1} \right]$$

which is the rippled-wall amplifier; it is easy to see why it was called the reduction-factor amplifier by Birdsall and Whinnery [56]. Birdsall [52] later published some experimental work on this device, which is dealt with in Section 3.2.3, but he re-named it.

It is also possible to obtain amplification if only V_0 is kept constant, for then Eqn 3.12 becomes

$$\left| \frac{V_c}{V_a} \right| = \left[\frac{p_2}{p_1} \right] \cdot \left[\frac{b_1}{b_2} \right]$$

At about the time that Peter, Bloom and Ruetz published their work other workers were also quite independently working on this type of device known as the rippled-stream amplifier [Birdsall, 52] or the scalloped-beam amplifier [Mihran 57, Bloom 58]. This work is dealt with in Section 3.2.4.

The usefulness of the transmission-line analogy is limited and so far as is known, no other papers have been published on the subject (it is used more frequently, however, in travelling-wave tube work). The analogue is such that the power must be supplied in such a way that the space-charge waves are excited at the point where I is zero and V is finite. In any case, the theory as given in Section 3.2.2.1 applies to the case in which there is a strong axial magnetic field confining motion to the z direction and yet we later talk about a beam with a variable radius without considering the rectilinear equivalent with a.c. surface charge density. Nevertheless, this is an interesting aspect of space-charge waves and at least suggests that one should investigate the other two possible types of space-charge-wave amplifiers.

3.2.3. The rippled-wall amplifier (the reduction-factor amplifier)

Birdsall and Whinnery [56] briefly referred to the possibilities of producing such a device. They were thinking in terms of the admittance of the wall surrounding the beam, work we will discuss in detail later (Section 3.2.5), but gave little theoretical justification for their statements. Much more detailed information was published a little later by Birdsall [52] and it is his work that is reported in Sections 3.2.3.1 and 3.2.3.2.

3.2.3.1. *The model*

The simple model is shown in Figure 42. The important factor is p_1/p_2, and in this case the other factors in the equation for G:

$$G = \left[\frac{V_{01}}{V_{02}}\right]^{\frac{3}{4}} \cdot \left[\frac{b_2}{b_1}\right] \cdot \left[\frac{p_1}{p_2}\right] \qquad \text{(Eqn. 3.12)}$$

are unity.

Birdsall showed that the gain is

$$= \frac{40}{\pi} \frac{\omega_p}{u_0} \left[\frac{1}{p_1} + \frac{1}{p_2}\right]^{-1} \log_{10}\left(\frac{p_1}{p_2}\right) \text{ dB/metre}$$

$$= \frac{40}{\pi} \frac{\omega_p}{u_0} F(p_1 p_2) \text{ dB/metre}$$

where

$$F(p_1 p_2) = \left(\frac{1}{p_1} + \frac{1}{p_2}\right)^{-1} \log_{10}\left(\frac{p_1}{p_2}\right).$$

The value of $F(p_1 p_2)$ is obtained from the curves of p versus b/a for $\gamma_0 b$ as a parameter, given earlier (Section 2.2.4, Figure 8b) and curves of $F(p_1 p_2)$ versus βb for various radii of the smallest part of the tube (a_2) are shown in Figure 43. The maximum obtainable gain is obtained

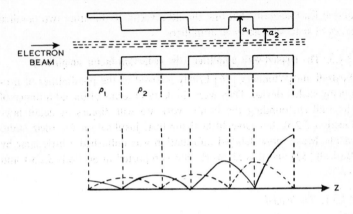

ELECTRON BEAM

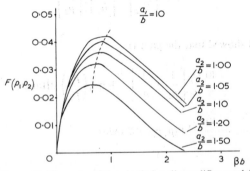

——— CURRENT MODULATION

- - - - - VELOCITY MODULATION

Figure 42. A simple model of the rippled-wall amplifier

Figure 43. The gain of the rippled-wall-amplifier model

in the range of $\beta b = 0.7$ to 0.9. For $a_2/b = 1$, the gain is

$$\frac{40}{\pi} \times 0.042 \frac{\omega_p}{u_0} \text{ dB/metre.}$$

This is approximately $\frac{1}{6}$th of the gain obtained in the double-stream amplifier (Section 3.3), but the rippled-wall amplifier is simpler.

3.2.3.2. *Experimental work*

To demonstrate the existence of rippled-wall amplification, a tube was constructed of six sections, each a quarter-plasma-wavelength long. Two helices were used to modulate and de-modulate the beam.

The gain was measured in two ways. Firstly, by comparing the rippled-wall system with a perfectly conducting smooth drift-tube, and secondly by measuring the gain *versus* the rippled-wall potential at several values of beam current and frequency. The helices were held at a constant potential of between 700 V and 800 V. The results obtained are shown

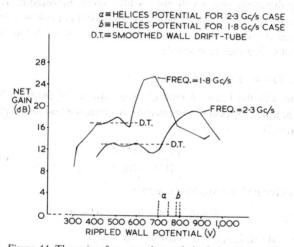

Figure 44. The gain of an experimental rippled-wall amplifier

in Figure 44, and the peaks obtained were attributed to the rippled wall. So far as can be ascertained this is the only rippled-wall amplifier constructed and these experiments the only ones performed on such a device.

3.2.4. Scalloped-beam amplification

Of the three types of space-charge-wave amplifiers mentioned so far, the scalloped-beam amplifier has received by far and away the most attention. Birdsall and Whinnery [56] first referred to it and then Birdsall [52] published brief details of some design data. The simple analysis of Peter, Bloom and Ruetz [55] was published soon after Bloom [58] gave a more detailed analysis in an unpublished R.C.A. technical report. Mihran [57] also reported some experimental work and some time later gave more details of his experiments [Mihran, 59]. It also appears that Rich and Rydbeck and Agder were working on the same subject, but the author has been unable to obtain copies of their reports.

Bloom, in his unpublished report, used a different approach to that already discussed, one which gives a little more information. It is for this reason, and also because he did not publish his work in a Journal, that brief details of his analysis and results are given before the experimental data that is available.

3.2.4.1. *The theory and design data*

Starting with the Eqns 3.6 and 3.7 of his alternative analysis (Section 3.2.2), in which the beam is represented as a transmission line of periodic reactance, i.e.

$$dV/dz = jX_R I$$
$$dI/dz = jB_S V$$

Bloom obtained the Mathieu equation

$$d^2 I/dx^2 + (A - 2q \cos 2x)I = 0 \qquad 3.13$$

where $A = (2\lambda_s/\lambda_0)$; $q = k(A/2)$; $x = \pi z/\lambda_s$

λ_s = the wavelength of the sinusoidal variation of the reactance X_R

$X_R = X_0[1 - k \cos(2\pi z/\lambda_s)]$

X_0 = unperturbed reactance

k = amplitude of the variation of the reactance and is proportional to the degree of scalloping.

λ_0 = plasma wavelength of the unperturbed

beam = $2\rho/\sqrt{(X_0 B_S)}$.

Eqn 3.13 has solutions of the form $\phi(x) \exp(\pm \mu x)$, $\phi(x)$ being periodic in x and these are discussed in terms of the stability plot in Figure 45.

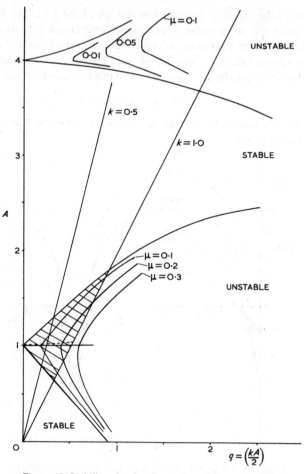

Figure 45. Stability plot for the scalloped-beam amplifier

The unstable regions are those in which the space-charge waves increase or decrease. Optimum growth or decay occurs when μ is largest (assuming it is real). Since k is always less than unity $k = (2q/A) < 1$. In

Figure 45, the region of interest is to the left of the $k=1$ line. For a given value of k, the q *versus* A line intersects the largest μ value when A is a little greater than unity, as can be seen from the locus of the optimum value of (λ_0/λ_s) – the dotted line. The amount by which A exceeds unity is usually less than 0·05 and if this is ignored it is seen that

$$2\lambda_s/\lambda_0 = 1 \quad \text{i.e.} \quad \lambda_s = \lambda_0/2 .$$

Thus for optimum gain the 'scallop' wavelength must be half of the unperturbed plasma wavelength.

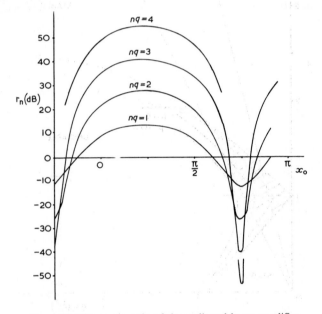

Figure 46. The power ratio of the scalloped-beam amplifier

Bloom solved Eqn 3.13 by considering the space-charge waves in a system consisting of sections of beam impedance (Section 3.2.2.1) alternating between Z_1 and Z_2, and found that the impedance wavelength is just half the mean plasma wavelength. He also showed that if the impedance is increased when the current is a maximum, amplification is obtained; and conversely, de-amplification is obtained if the impedance is decreased when the current is a maximum. For optimum growth or decay a current maximum should be at the point where the beam impedance is increasing or decreasing most rapidly. This is shown in Figure 46 where curves of the power ratio r_n *versus* x_0, the position of the current maximum with respect to the scalloping phase, with nq as parameter, are given; n is an integer and is the number of scallop wavelengths from x_0 to the point where the measurement is made. It is seen that the greater nq, which is equivalent to the larger the number of

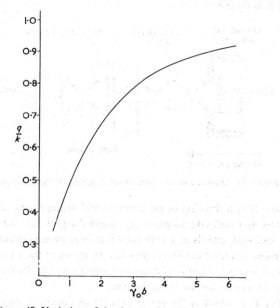

Figure 47. Variation of the degree of scalloping of a beam

scallop wavelengths or the greater the degree of scalloping, the greater the amplification or de-amplification. For optimum gain $r_n = \exp(n\pi q)$ and values of q (normalized by k, the percentage scalloping) *versus* $\gamma_0 b$ are given in Figure 47. These curves are used to calculate r_n from the above equation. Note that the plasma frequency reduction factor must be taken into account.

It is relevant to point out here that both the analyses given considered the 'stepped beam' case. According to Mihran, Rich, in his unpublished work, showed that the effect of charge density is $4/\pi$ more effective in the stepped beam case then it is in the sinusoidally scalloped beam.

3.2.4.2. *Experimental work*

The only known attempt to construct a device to verify the possibility of producing scalloped-beam amplification was by Mihran [57, 59], and his work is described below.

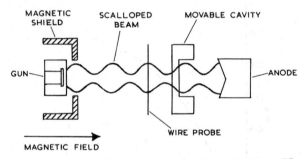

Figure 48. Drawing of an experimental scalloped-beam amplifier

Figure 48 is a drawing of his experimental arrangement. The beam, produced in a perfectly magnetically shielded region (i.e. the Brillouin flow condition), travels in a drift-tube free from external electric fields. A movable resonant cavity enables one to measure the r.f. current at any point along the beam. Mihran developed a special fine wire probe method of measuring the beam diameter.

Figure 49 is a plot of the power gain *versus* distance along the drift-tube, measured at 1,000 Mc/s, and also shows the variation of beam diameter along the drift-tube. Values of other variables are shown on the diagram. More than 10 dB gain was obtained in the drift-tube, equivalent to 2·0 to 2·5 dB per scallop. Since the cavity used was a fixed tuned type, the variation of gain with frequency of input signal could not be

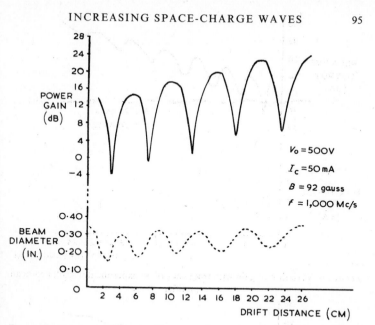

Figure 49. The measured gain of an experimental scalloped-beam amplifier

measured over a continuous frequency range. Two spot checks, at 1768 Mc/s and 2422 Mc/s, were made however and the results are shown in Figures 50 and 51. The scallop wavelength does not alter with frequency, but the plasma frequency reduction factor does alter. As the frequency is increased, the bunches are formed closer together and the effective plasma frequency is increased and the plasma wavelength is reduced. To maintain synchronism the magnetic field strength must be increased, and the graphs show that the number of scallops have increased. The gain per scallop in the two cases given was 2·0 dB and 2·1 dB respectively. Since these are approximately the same, the theory indicates that the degree of scalloping was unaltered. Thus, by merely altering the magnetic field strength, gain can be obtained over a large range of frequencies. If the magnetic field is reduced below the point at which optimum gain is obtained, the phase between the standing wave pattern on the beam

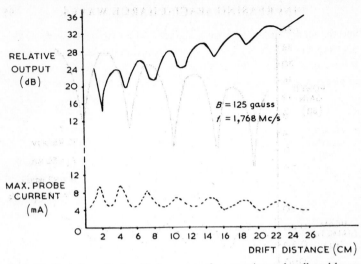

Figure 50. Variation of gain with frequency of an experimental scalloped-beam amplifier

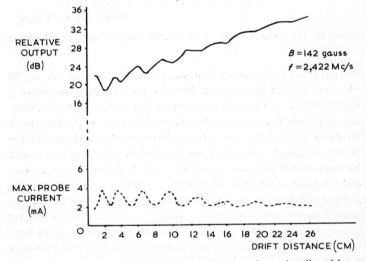

Figure 51. Variation of gain with frequency of an experimental scalloped-beam amplifier

and the scalloping of the beam is changed. The effect is shown in Figure 52. Here, the r.f. null point occurs when the beam diameter is a maximum instead of at the optimum position which is shown, and there is no gain in power along the beam. It is possible to reduce the magnetic field still

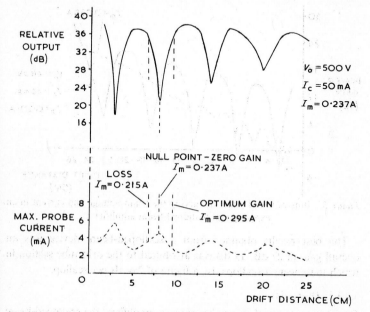

Figure 52. Variation of gain with longitudinal magnetic field strength of an experimental scalloped-beam amplifier

further, until the phase of the scalloping is 180° from the optimum at which point a loss is obtained.

Figure 53 shows the effect on the r.f. standing wave of varying the beam voltage and current. One case, in which the beam voltage = 480 V, beam current = 49 mA and the magnet current = 0·301 A, gives a gain of 2.5 dB per scallop. (Unfortunately the data given was insufficient to calculate the magnetic field strength.) The second case, in which the beam voltage = 155 V, beam current = 16 mA and the magnet current =

0·328 A, gives 2.6 dB gain per scallop. These results may be interpreted as implying that the maximum and minimum beam diameters are the same in both cases.

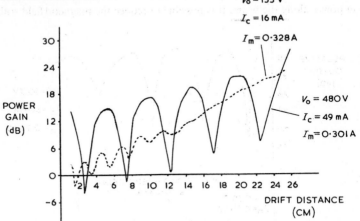

Figure 53. Illustration of effect of varying the beam voltage and current in an experimental scalloped-beam amplifier

The best results obtained from a scalloped-beam device was an overall gain of 27 dB: 17 dB was attributed to the drift-tube section in which there were 7 scallops, i.e. a figure of 2·4 dB per scallop.

3.2.4.3. *Discussion*

Of the three types of space-charge-wave amplifiers, the scalloped-beam type is theoretically the simplest. It requires no special drift-tubes or adjacent r.f. circuits, but only a method of applying the signal and removing it at the end. In practice, however, one can visualize difficulties over the production of a suitable stable beam with as large a degree of scalloping as possible. The velocity-jump and rippled-wall amplifiers do not have this problem as they both work with very high longitudinal magnetic fields. Although a lot of attention has been paid to this method of producing increasing space-charge waves, the only experimental work published is that reported here, and it is quite possible that the difficulties of producing the beam have been the limiting factor in the development of further devices of this type. Nevertheless, the theory has been used to account for some, otherwise inexplicable, observed experimental results as is seen in Section 3.3.3.2.

Finally, a physical explanation of the mechanism of scalloped-beam amplification can be given. Figure 54 shows the system which is considered to be a stepped-beam system as in Section 3.2.2.2.

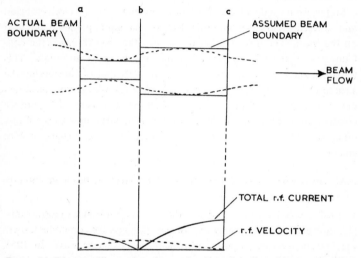

Figure 54. Diagram illustrating the mechanism of scalloped-beam amplification

Suppose that an electron bunch is at plane a and it is such that the total r.f. current is a maximum at this point and the a.c. velocities are zero. As the bunch travels further, there is a decrease in current until at a point a quarter-plasma wavelength further on the r.f. current is zero (at plane b). Here, however, the beam electrons have acquired a.c. velocities. At this point, the beam is suddenly expanded and the debunching forces are therefore reduced. Consequently, the electrons (which have a.c. velocities) move closer together than was previously the case. This takes longer than before and the result is that at plane c, the total r.f. current is higher than it was at plane a. If at plane c the beam is suddenly returned to its original diameter, the same number of electrons are placed in a smaller volume than at a and hence the r.f. component of the current is increased. This is, therefore, in effect, a method of producing a large d.c. current density in the region of the beam in which de-bunching occurs and a low d.c. current density where bunching occurs.

So far, we have devoted our attention primarily to the electron beam and concerned ourselves with the effects of changes in potential and field on the beam. The investigation has shown that in two cases, the configuration of the drift-tube surrounding the beam is important. This leads one naturally to ask if another approach, that of considering the structure surrounding the beam, would be fruitful. We are not concerned in this monograph with propagating structures such as the helix, but we conduct an investigation into non-propagating structures to see if any other possible methods of producing increasing space-charge waves emerge.

3.2.5. Increasing space-charge waves in an electron beam in non-propagating structures

In 1951, Pierce [60] showed that if the circuit admittance of a transmission line near a beam is inductive, or has a dissipative component, there may be an increasing and a decreasing space-charge wave. In 1953, Birdsall and Whinnery [56] also suggested that beams moving in simple non-propagating structures might support increasing space-charge waves.

It was reasonable to assume that this was so because at the 1950 Conference on Electron Tubes, Walker reported that an inductive-wall device, called the 'Easitron' had been operated satisfactorily. Birdsall, at the same conference, disclosed that a resistive-wall device had also been made to work satisfactorily. Before proceeding to analyze these two special methods of producing increasing space-charge waves, it is interesting to make a general field study for walls of complex admittances. In view of the success Pierce [60] had with the method of matching wave admittances at the beam boundary, when he was analyzing the travelling-wave tube and some propagating structures, it was reasonable to assume that this method would be enlightening. Birdsall and Whinnery [56] used this approach and an outline of their analysis is given below.

3.2.5.1. *An electron beam in general admittance walls*

It is assumed, that the electron beam is in a coaxial cylindrical tube, in the rectilinear flow condition (infinite longitudinal magnetic focusing field) and that there is positive ion neutralization. Only small signals are considered. There is a cylindrically symmetric field and a complex representation is used.

Eqn 2.56 is

$$\frac{1}{r}\frac{\partial}{\partial r}\left(r\frac{\partial E_z}{\partial r}\right) - \tau_2^2 E_z = 0 \qquad (2.56)$$

where

$$\tau_2^2 = \gamma^2 \frac{\left[\dfrac{\omega_p^2}{\omega_b^2} - 1\right]}{\left[\dfrac{\omega_p^2}{\omega_0^2} - 1\right]}$$

and where $\omega_b = (\omega - \gamma u_0)$; $\omega_0^2 = \omega_b^2 - 4\Omega^2$; $\Omega = \eta(r_c^2 B_c/2r^2)$.

If $\omega_0^2 = \infty$ (the rectilinear flow case) this gives

$$\tau_2^2 = -\gamma^2\left[\frac{\omega_p^2}{\omega_b^2} - 1\right] = -T^2 \qquad (cf.\ \text{Eqn 2.13}) \qquad 3.14$$

and the solution is

$$E_z = A'J_0(Tr).$$

But

$$H_\theta = \frac{\omega\varepsilon_0}{\gamma}E_r = \frac{\omega\varepsilon_0}{\gamma}\frac{j}{\gamma}\frac{\partial E_z}{\partial r} \quad \text{(Eqns A3.6 and A3.7)}$$

(assuming $\gamma^2 \gg k^2$)

therefore

$$H_\theta = \frac{j\omega\varepsilon_0}{\gamma^2}.A'.T.J_1(Tr).$$

Now the beam admittance Y_b, is defined by H_θ/E_z and

$$\frac{H_\theta}{E_z} = \frac{j\omega\varepsilon_0}{\gamma^2} \cdot T \cdot \frac{J_1(Tr)}{J_0(Tr)} = Y_b .$$

For correct boundary conditions at $r = b$, i.e. the beam filling the tube, Y_b must equal the wall admittance Y_W

therefore
$$Y_W = \frac{j\omega\varepsilon_0}{\gamma^2} \cdot T \cdot \frac{J_1(Tb)}{J_0(Tb)}$$

therefore
$$(Tb)\frac{J_1(Tb)}{J_0(Tb)} = \frac{\gamma^2 b^2}{j\omega\varepsilon_0 b} Y_W . \qquad 3.15$$

The problem now is to solve Eqn 3.15 for γ given the wall admittance Y_W, remembering, of course, that γ may be complex. Various methods have been adopted. Chu and Jackson [61] used the first term of the expansions of the Bessel functions $J_1(Tb)$ and $J_0(Tb)$ to obtain a simple algebraic equation. They point out, however, that these expansions assume that E_z does not vary with r. This would give $T^2 E_z = 0$ [Eqn 2.56] rather a severe restriction. Birdsall and Whinnery defined (Tb) as $\gamma_0 b(m+jn)$ and produced a map of $(Tb)J_1(Tb)/J_0(Tb)$ *versus* the real and imaginary parts of (Tb) [Map I – not shown].

A general solution of the Eqn 3.15 for γ is difficult because there are two unknowns, γ and Y_W, and consequently some approximations have to be made. Once again we assume that $\gamma \simeq \gamma_0$ so that $Y_W(\gamma) \simeq Y_W(\gamma_0)$ and now T can be simply determined.

Eqn 3.14 gives
$$\gamma = \gamma_0 \pm \frac{\omega_p}{u_0}\left[1 + \frac{T^2}{\gamma_0^2}\right]^{-\frac{1}{2}}$$

or we may write
$$\gamma = \gamma_0 \pm (\bar{p}+jq)\frac{\omega_p}{u_0} \qquad 3.16$$

therefore
$$(\bar{p}+jq) = \left[1+(m+jn)^2\right]^{-\frac{1}{2}} \qquad 3.17$$

and $\bar{p}$ and q are plotted in the m and n plane (fourth quadrant only). [Map 2 – not shown].

Eqn 3.16 indicates that in this method we look for a plasma frequency reduction factor that may be complex, i.e. $(\bar{p}+jq)$. If the reduction factor happens to be real, it becomes equal to $\bar{p}$ ($q=0$) as in the perfectly conducting drift-tube example ($\bar{p}=p$). For increasing space-charge waves, $q>0$; q is the gain factor. Map 2 is used in conjunction with Map 1 to obtain the gain of the system under consideration. A suitable method is to:

(a) Find the wall admittance H_θ/E_z in terms of ω, u_0 and γ.

(b) Put $(Tb)J_1(Tb)/J_0(Tb)=x\exp(j\xi)=f(Tb)$ and find x and ξ from

$$x\,e^{j\xi} = [(\gamma_0 b)^2/(j\omega\varepsilon_0 b)]\,Y_W\ .$$

(c) Find $(Tb)=\gamma_0 b(m+jn)$ from Map 1.

(d) Find $\bar{p}$ and q from Map 2 and the appropriate values of m and n.

(e) Find gain $=8\cdot69(\omega_p/u_0)q$ (dB/metre)

and
$$u_p = \cfrac{u_0}{\left[1 + \bar{p}\,\dfrac{\omega_p}{\omega}\right]}\ .$$

3.2.5.2. *Some special cases*

It is now possible to consider some special cases and for simplicity let the beam fill the tube. [In practice, of course, the beam does not necessarily fill the tube, and it is necessary to equate the wave admittance of the beam with that presented at the edge of the beam by the wall. (Y_W is modified by the space between the wall and the edge of the beam.)]

Putting $Y_W=M+jN$ consider the following:

(a) Infinite admittance walls – the beam is in a perfectly conducting drift-tube – $Y_W=\infty$. Here $q=0$ and there is no gain, as observed in Section 2.2.2.

(b) Zero admittance walls – $Y_W=0$. Here (Tb) takes the eigen-values corresponding to $(x+\frac{1}{4})\pi$ where $x=1, 2\ldots$ Again there is no gain and this corresponds to the extended beam as in Section 2.2.3.

(c) Capacitive wall admittance – let $Y_W=jN$ where $N>0$. Eqn 3.15 shows that T is real and so there is no gain, which is consistent with γ being real. There are an infinite number of values of (Tb).

(d) Inductive wall admittance – here $Y_W = -jN$ and Eqn 3.15 becomes

$$(Tb)\frac{J_1(Tb)}{J_0(Tb)} = -\frac{(\gamma_0 b)^2}{\omega\varepsilon_0 b} N = f(Tb).$$

Therefore, $f(Tb)$ must be a negative real number.

Since $Tb = \gamma_0 b(m+jn)$:

If $n > -1$ Eqn 3.17 shows that on the imaginary axis, $m=0$, there is no gain or attenuation (i.e. $q=0$). Note that in this case $\bar{p} > 1$ so that the effective plasma frequency is increased.

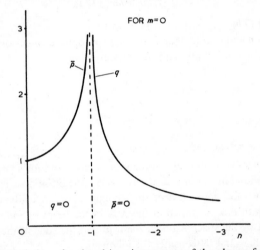

Figure 55. Variation of real and imaginary parts of the plasma frequency reduction factor for an electron beam moving in an inductive wall.

If $n < -1$ Eqn 3.17 shows that there is gain since $q > 0$ but that $\bar{p} = 0$ which means that the phase velocity of the space-charge wave equals the electron velocity.

If $n = -1$ there is an infinite gain.

Figure 55 shows the values of $\bar{p}$ and q *versus* n on the imaginary axis $m=0$.

(e) Resistive wall admittance – here $Y_w = M$ and

$$(Tb)\frac{J_1(Tb)}{J_0(Tb)} = \frac{(\gamma_0 b)^2 M}{j\omega\varepsilon_0 b}.$$

This leads to a growing wave. Figure 56 is a plot of the gain factor q against the parameter $(\omega\varepsilon_0 b)/M$ for different values of $(\gamma_0 b)$.

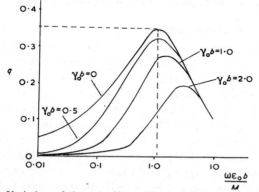

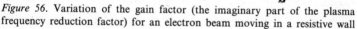

Figure 56. Variation of the gain factor (the imaginary part of the plasma frequency reduction factor) for an electron beam moving in a resistive wall

It is seen that the maximum value of q (q_{max}) obtainable is when $\gamma_0 b = 0$ and this is found at $(\omega\varepsilon_0 b)/M = 2/\sqrt{3}$; q_{max} is in fact $= 1/(2\sqrt{2})$. This figure is comparable to that obtained from the double-stream amplifier (Section 3.3).

3.2.5.3. *Discussion*

The analysis in Sections 3.2.5.1 and 3.2.5.2 indicates that walls with zero, infinite and capacitive admittance do not support increasing waves. So far as zero and infinite admittances are concerned, this merely substantiates the evidence of Section 2.2 which showed that γ had an attenuation constant equal to zero. The Birdsall and Whinnery analysis also shows that walls with resistive admittance support increasing waves and that walls with inductive admittance, in some circumstances, also support increasing waves. Resistive-wall and inductive-wall devices are discussed in more detail in Sections 3.2.6 and 3.2.7. Before doing so, however, we should note that although walls of zero, infinite and capacitive admittance do not support increasing waves when used alone, they can be used to produce increasing waves when used in tandem. The gain turns out to be dependent on $\bar{p}$, the real part of the reduction factor (the phase factor). This is the reduction-factor amplifier, later re-named the rippled-wall amplifier [Birdsall, 52], Section 3.2.3.

3.2.6. The resistive-wall amplifier

Details of the first practical devices produced were published by Birdsall, Brewer and Haeff [62]. They were constructed after their attempts to reduce the noise in travelling-wave tubes by passing the beam near a lossy circuit, the object being to absorb the noise energy before the beam enters the interaction region. In the light of more recent knowledge, we know that only fast wave noise can be removed in this way and, therefore, this is of no value in the travelling-wave tube (Section 5.1.3). During this work Chu [63] suggested to the authors that the opposite effect, namely amplification, might take place in these circumstances. Combined with the work of Pierce [60], already referred to in Section 3.2.5, this encouraged Birdsall and his co-workers to pursue the possibility.

In this device, as in other space-charge-wave amplifiers, there is no interaction between the beam and a circuit wave as in the travelling-wave tube. The amplification is obtained from the interaction between the charge on the beam, and the charge induced on to the wall by the charge on the beam. This interaction causes the electron bunches in the beam to increase in size and the result is an exponential increase, in space, of the signal. It is helpful to introduce the subject by considering a simple one-dimensional model.

3.2.6.1. *A simple model*

In this model, an electron beam flows through a medium that has conductivity σ as well as the usual dielectric properties (i.e. the dielectric constant is $\varepsilon = \varepsilon_0 \varepsilon'$ where ε' is the relative dielectric constant). The medium is porous so that the beam passes through it without interruption. This model is referred to as the resistive-medium amplifier, (R.M.A.)

The usual assumptions are made and since it is the now familiar type of analysis only brief details are given.

Eqns A1.2, A1.10 and the continuity equation are used:

$$\nabla \times \mathbf{H} = \frac{\partial \mathbf{D}}{\partial t} + \mathbf{J} \tag{A1.2}$$

$$\nabla \cdot \mathbf{D} = \rho \tag{A1.10}$$

$$\nabla \cdot \mathbf{J} = -\frac{\partial \rho}{\partial t} \tag{continuity}$$

It is assumed that the conducting medium has free charges (induced by the charge of the beam) of density ρ_m; let the beam charge density be ρ_s.

If the total current density

$$J = J_s + \sigma E \tag{3.18}$$

we have

$$\nabla \cdot J_s + \partial \rho_s / \partial t = 0$$

and

$$\nabla \cdot \sigma E + \frac{\partial}{\partial t}(\rho - \rho_s) = 0 . \tag{3.19}$$

Note $\rho = \rho_m + \rho_s$.

Since a.c. quantities vary as $\exp(j\omega t)$, Eqns A1.10 and 3.19 give

$$\rho_m = -\rho_s \left[1 + \frac{j\omega\varepsilon}{\sigma} \right]^{-1} \tag{3.20}$$

The wave equation

$$\nabla^2 E - \mu\varepsilon \frac{\partial^2 E}{\partial t^2} = \frac{1}{\varepsilon} \nabla \cdot \rho + \mu \frac{\partial J}{\partial t}$$

combined with Eqn 3.20 becomes

$$\nabla_{r\theta}^2 E_z + T^2 E_z = 0$$

where $T^2 = (\gamma^2 - \omega^2 \mu\varepsilon + j\omega\mu\sigma) \left[\dfrac{\omega_p^2}{u_0^2(\gamma - \gamma_0)^2 \dfrac{\varepsilon}{\varepsilon_0}\left(1 + \dfrac{\sigma}{j\omega\varepsilon}\right)} - 1 \right]$.

But since $\nabla^2_{r\theta} E_z = 0$, T, must be zero for E_z to exist and this gives

(a) $\gamma^2 = \omega^2 \mu\sigma - j\omega\mu\sigma$ which implies no boundaries

and (b):

$$\frac{\omega_p^2}{u_0^2} = (\gamma - \gamma_0)^2 \frac{\varepsilon}{\varepsilon_0} \left[1 + \frac{\sigma}{j\omega\varepsilon} \right]$$

Solution (a) gives a pair of field waves (Section 2.2.2.3). They are decaying and are only important in determining feedback in the opposite direction to that of the electron beam. Solution (b) gives

$$\gamma = \gamma_0 \pm \frac{\omega_p}{u_0 \left[\varepsilon' \left(1 - \frac{j\sigma}{\omega\varepsilon} \right) \right]^{\frac{1}{2}}} \qquad 3.21$$

The positive sign in Eqn 3.21 indicates that

(i) γ has a positive imaginary part, and

(ii) γ has a real part which is greater than γ_0, i.e. the phase velocity is less than that of the velocity of the beam.

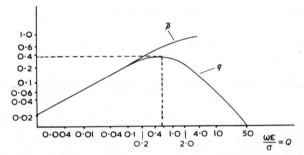

Figure 57. Variation of phase and gain factors of the resistive-medium amplifier

These are the conditions required for amplification. Thus the analysis indicates that an increasing wave may be produced. Note that the other wave of this conjugate pair is a decreasing wave.

Suppose

$$\left[1 - \frac{j\sigma}{\omega\varepsilon} \right]^{-\frac{1}{2}} = \bar{p} + jq$$

then Eqn 3.21 becomes

$$\gamma = \gamma_0 \pm \frac{\omega_p}{u_0} (\bar{p}+jq) \cdot \frac{1}{\sqrt{\varepsilon'}} \qquad 3.22$$

which is similar to Eqn 3.16. Curves of q the gain factor and $\bar{p}$ the phase factor *versus* $\frac{\omega\varepsilon}{\sigma}(=Q)$ for this case are given in Figure 57.

The phase velocity of the increasing wave is given by

$$u_p = \frac{u_0}{1 + \dfrac{\bar{p}\omega_p}{\omega\sqrt{\varepsilon'}}}$$

and the rate of increase of the increasing wave is

$$8\cdot69 \frac{\omega_p}{\omega} \frac{q}{\sqrt{\varepsilon'}} \text{ dB/metre} \qquad 3.24$$

3.2.6.2. *Design data*

The rate of gain is a maximum when $q=1/(2\sqrt{2})$ (see Figure 57) at the point $\omega\varepsilon/\sigma=1/\sqrt{3}$.

Therefore the maximum rate of gain is approximately $3\dfrac{\omega_p}{\omega\sqrt{\varepsilon'}}$ dB/metre [Eqn 3.24] and this is comparable with that obtained from the double stream amplifier (Section 3.3).

Gain is obtained over a large range of frequencies (Figure 57). For a tube with a 35 dB gain (no initial loss) the points at which the loss is 3 dB down occur at 50% and 170% of the optimum point; a 120% bandwidth.

The variation of gain with ε/σ, which is a property of the resistive material only, is not critical. If σ is increased by a factor of 2 over the optimum value, q is reduced by only 10%. Since the gain is proportional to $q/\sqrt{\varepsilon'}$ it is desirable to keep ε' as small as possible.

In the frequency range 0·1 to 100 Gc/s, the optimum value of σ/ε' is from 10^{-2} to 10 and this is of the same order as for semiconductors. (For good conductors it is 10^7 and for good insulators it is 10^{-12}).

3.2.6.3. *The practical model*

Figure 58 is a drawing of the practical model which corresponds to a single pore R.M.A. The beam is constrained to move only in the z direction by a strong longitudinal d.c. magnetic field. The dielectric constant of the glass supporting the resistive coating (relative dielectric constant ε'') is assumed to be equal to that of free space, i.e. $\varepsilon'' = \varepsilon_0$.

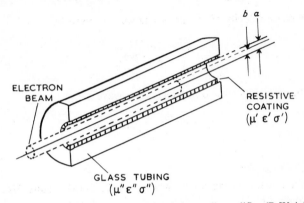

Figure 58. A model of a practical resistive-wall amplifier (R.W.A.)

The analysis is given in Sections 3.2.6.1 and 3.2.6.2 and equations 3.22, 3.23 and 3.24 apply with $\varepsilon' = 1$. Curves of $2\pi\omega b^2 \varepsilon_0 R'$ *versus* $(\gamma_0 b)$ are plotted, for constant values of $\bar{p}$ and q, for the case of the beam filling the tube in Figure 59. R' is the resistance per unit length of the resistive coating.

3.2.6.4. *Comparison of the two models*

The theoretical properties of the R.M.A. and the practical model (R.W.A.) are tabulated in Table 1. It is seen that the gain of the R.W.A. is lower than that of the R.M.A. by a large factor. In some experimental devices constructed by Birdsall and his co-workers it is lower still, due to the higher dielectric constant of the glass tubing which produces a capacitive shunting effect. It was found that part of this loss is re-gained if honeycombed structures are used.

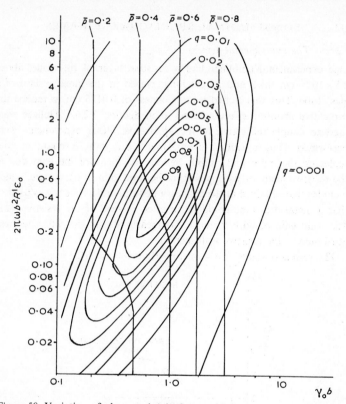

Figure 59. Variation of phase and gain factors of the practical resistive-wall-amplifier model

Table 1

	R.M.A.	R.W.A.
Maximum gain factor (for $\varepsilon' = \varepsilon'' = \varepsilon_0$)	0·351	0·10
Bandwidth between half power frequencies no initial loss —35 dB maximum gain	120%	70%
Dependance of gain on resistive-wall potential	none	±50% to Go 3 dB down from 35 dB

3.2.6.5. *The experimental devices*

One experimental amplifier had a resistive layer of tin oxide, about 2.5×10^{-5} cm thick and 25 cm long, placed in the inner surface of a glass tube. This was etched to a thickness of 0·0125 cm to reduce the capacitive shunting effect referred to in Section 3.2.6.4. Helices were used to couple the signal to the apparatus. Other experiments were performed using a similar arrangement, but with resonant cavities replacing the input and output helices. To measure the gain due to the resistive medium, as opposed to the total gain of the system, which includes that obtained at the helices, a demountable system was used so that a metal drift-tube could be inserted instead of the resistive wall. The total gain of both systems was measured and the difference was attributed to the resistive wall section.

The results obtained are shown in Figures 60 to 64.

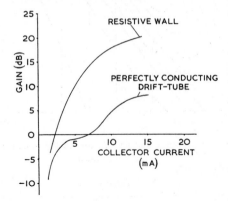

Figure 60. The gain of a helix coupled resistive-wall amplifier

Figure 60 is a plot of the overall gain of the helix coupled tube as a function of collector current, for both the drift-tube and the resistive wall. The gain of the perfectly conducting drift-tube is assumed to be due to the helices. The gain obtained from the resistive wall is approximately 10 dB for collector currents of from 10 mA to 17 mA. This was at 3 Gc/s. From measured operating parameters (not quoted in the paper), a value of 0·035 for q was obtained compared with the theoretical value of 0·031 (not calculated in the paper).

Figure 61 is a plot of the gain *versus* the resistive wall potential of a helix coupled tube. The gain changes very little over the range 300 V to 1,000 V. Two curves are plotted, being the maxima and the minima, and

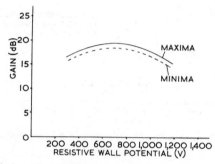

Figure 61. Variation of gain with resistive-wall potential of a helix coupled resistive-wall amplifier

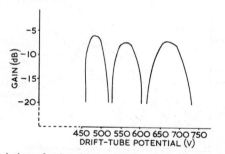

Figure 62. Variation of gain with conducting drift-tube potential of a cavity coupled resistive-wall amplifier

the appearance of these is due to the fact that constructive and destructive interference between the two space-charge waves is obtainable. For a 3 dB drop in gain a 22% variation of voltage at peak gain was obtained.

Graphs of the gain obtained from the cavity coupled tube, as a function of collector current, for both the resistive wall and the drift-tube gave very similar curves to those of Figure 60 (which are for the helix coupled tube). They showed that at 10 mA cathode current, the resistive

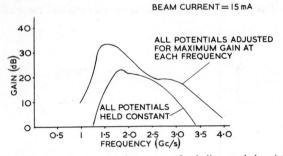

Figure 63. Variation of gain with frequency for a helix coupled resistive-wall amplifier

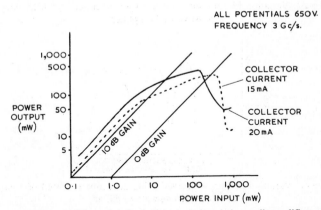

Figure 64. The gain of a helix coupled resistive-wall amplifier

wall section gave a gain of approximately 12 dB which is equivalent to a gain factor of 0·034. This was measured at 2·920 Gc/s. The variation of gain with resistive wall potential for the cavity coupled tube, is very similar to that for the helix coupled tube (Figure 61), and the variation of the gain obtained from a drift-tube is given in Figure 62. This is of course the cavity-coupled klystron and the curves indicate the interference obtained between the two unattenuated space-charge waves.

Variation of gain with frequency in a helix coupled tube is shown in Figure 63. This is for a fixed beam current of 15 mA. The bandwidth is about 700 Mc/s between half power frequencies if all potentials are held constant. This experiment was performed with a special sealed tube, as opposed to the demountable tube, and the results of further experiments made with this tube are shown in Figure 64. These show power output *versus* power input at beam currents of 15 mA and 20 mA with all potentials at 650 V, the measurements being made at 3 Gc/s.

3.2.6.6. *Discussion*

It was shown theoretically (Section 3.2.6.1) that providing $\sigma > 0$ a pair of space-charge waves, one increasing, the other decreasing, are possible. The experimental work showed beyond doubt that increasing waves can be obtained from a resistive wall, since there was a substantial drop in gain when the resistive wall section was replaced by a perfectly conducting drift-tube. The work of Cutler and Quate [41] (Section 2.5.2) was verified by the drift-tube experiments of Birdsall *et al.*, all of which supported the view that interference between the two unattenuated space-charge waves is possible. It is also evident from the interference patterns that there are both increasing and decreasing waves in the resistive wall section.

Finally, it can be seen that any system of this nature used for attenuating a signal by means of the decreasing wave (and this was attempted), would also result in the setting up of the increasing wave precisely as Chu suggested. It might be possible, with very special input conditions, to set up only the decreasing wave, but it is unlikely, to say the least, that noise would only excite the decreasing wave.

3.2.7. Inductive-wall amplification – the Easitron

So far as can be ascertained, the only work on this subject is due to Walker. In 1950 he published two internal memoranda entitled *The Easitron* and *Some Easitron Amplifier Structures*. These memoranda [64] have been quoted by various authors, but little information has been reproduced.

His work is mainly theoretical and very little information on his experiments was given. A drawing of his apparatus and a gain *versus* frequency curve were given (Figures 65 and 66), but unfortunately he

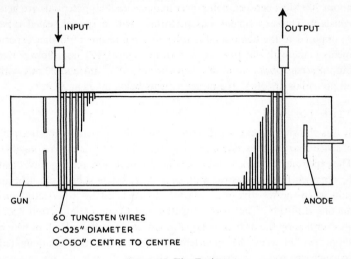

Figure 65. The Easitron

barely described them. Nevertheless, it was shown theoretically that if the wall admittance was capacitive two unattenuated space-charge waves exist. If, however, the wall is inductive, a conjugate pair of waves, one increasing and one decreasing, are obtained.

Walker showed that in a strip beam propagating in a strong longitudinal magnetic field, the propagation constant was given by

$$\gamma = -\frac{\omega}{u_0} \pm j \sqrt{\left(\frac{\omega_p^2}{u_0} \Delta x\right)} \cdot \sqrt{\left(\frac{\omega \varepsilon_0}{-B_s}\right)}$$

where Δx = thickness of the beam

and B_s = susceptance per unit length.

He showed that the beam and the inductive wall constitute something

like a continuous multi-gap klystron without drift spaces. By its interaction with the circuit the beam becomes progressively more bunched.
This is similar to the travelling-wave tube, but in that case the circuit
is a propagating circuit – it has a mode of propagation in the absence of
the beam and the energy is continually being extracted from the beam

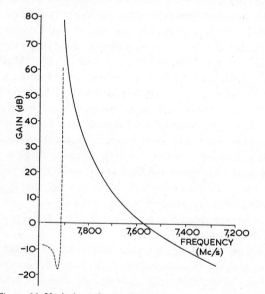

Figure 66. Variation of gain with frequency of the Easitron

to flow into the circuit. In contrast, the Easitron operates without an
interchange of energy between the beam and the inductive wall.

Two possible practical devices were mentioned: a row of half-wave
resonant wires placed between the centre lines of two conducting sheets,
and a row of pill-box cavities which the beam passes through. The
'wire' system, shown in Figure 65, is that which Walker used in his
experiments. It is a pity that no further information is available and one
can only presume that Walker felt that it was not worth proceeding
with. Why it was called the 'Easitron' is a mystery, although Kompfner

[65] suggested that it was because of its uncritical nature, which made it 'easy' to work.

3.2.8. Final discussion

Much of the theory of increasing space-charge waves given in the previous sections has severe limitations. Perhaps the most striking is the fact that to show that increasing waves could be obtained on a rippled beam, a model assuming that electrons have no radial velocity component was devised. It is obvious that a theory taking radial velocity into account presents problems, indeed as recently as 1961 Mueller [66], in a very sophisticated analysis, attempted to deduce facts about a rippled beam from a theory applied to a smooth electron beam. In addition, the theories also dealt with a 'stepped beam' model instead of a sinusoidally varying beam (which was apparently dealt with by Rich); a more realistic model. It is not proposed to pursue this subject further, because it appears that a more rigid explanation involves coupling between space-charge waves and field waves; this involves two subjects outside the scope of this monograph. Note, however, that this suggests that there is little difference between the travelling-wave tube and wall admittance devices. Branch's work (Section 2.2.4 and Figure 9) also indicated that this may be so.

Despite these limitations, the experimental results obtained agreed in all cases with the theories sufficiently to justify the conclusion that the behaviour of the increasing space-charge wave was much as predicted.

On the surface, each of the devices had some useful features that would have justified pursuing their possibilities still further, and it may seem surprising that little other work has been reported. It is difficult to give a reason for this because, on the whole, the data given in this series of papers is unfortunately insufficient to draw conclusions about this point. (This is a pity in view of the limited amount of literature available, especially as in one case the authors state that '. . . design data have been worked out but are not given . . .'). From information available, it is evident that one major difficulty in all cases is that of excitation. The lack of published work on this subject is in marked contrast to the subject of propagation of space-charge waves near propagating circuits in which there is a profusion of theoretical and experimental data.

The work of Rigrod and Lewis (Section 2.3) showed that two unattenuated space-charge waves propagate on a beam in the Brillouin flow condition (no magnetic flux linking the cathode). It is now possible to see that, as some rippling is obtained on a beam in Brillouin flow, one might have expected their analysis to show that an increasing space-charge wave propagates on the beam (Section 3.2.4). That it did not may be due to the fact that a rectilinear flow model was used (in which only unattenuated waves are obtained) and the rippling of the beam was taken into account by the assumption that a surface charge density existed. This discrepancy may well lead one to suspect the validity of Rigrod and Lewis's arguments, but it must be said that many workers have since accepted that basically the method is satisfactory. We are left, therefore, with this, as yet, unresolved anomaly and one that cannot be resolved without a detailed fundamental study of electron beam technology; it is not proposed to undertake this.

Although we have studied the various effects independently, it is obvious that combinations of two or more of these effects are possible. For example, if the drift-tube is of constant diameter, the predominant factor in the equation for the gain [Eqn 3.12] is b_1/b_2. Therefore, by increasing b_1/b_2 the gain can be increased; b_1/b_2 can be made quite large. In contrast to this p_2/p_1 cannot be made very large. If $b_1/b_2 > 1$, $p_2/p_1 < 1$ and the two effects cancel each other out. It is necessary to make b_1 large (in terms of electronic wavelengths) if the (p_2/p_1) factor is not to cancel out the gain due to the factor (b_1/b_2). On the whole it is found experimentally that the scalloped-beam amplifier can be made to produce an overall gain of approximately three times the overall gain of the R.W.A.

It was noted (Section 3.2.6.4) that in the experimental resistive-wall amplifier, the effect of the capacitive shunting of the resistive wall (by, in this case, glass) is to reduce the gain considerably. Thus, although a capacitive wall by itself has no affect, one in tandem with a resistive wall does have an affect. It may well be that the combination of different effects, examples of which have been given above, reduces the potentially good values of amplification to mediocre values, which limits the usefulness of these devices.

Despite the limitations of the practical devices and the unsatisfactory theoretical explanations of their operation, this is an interesting subject and it is a vital part of the history of the development of space-charge-wave theory. Similar analytical methods are used to explain the operation of the travelling-wave tube and there is no doubt that the operation of such tubes can be adequately explained in terms of increasing space-charge waves. One can only conclude, therefore, that it is only for want of more effort that more satisfactory explanations are not available. There is no doubt, however, that it is possible to obtain increasing space-charge waves on single electron beams without using propagating structures.

3.3 INCREASING SPACE-CHARGE WAVES ON TWO ELECTRON BEAMS

Although it was logical to discuss increasing space-charge waves on single electron beams first, historically, the earliest investigations on the possibility of obtaining increasing space-charge waves on electron beams were made on systems containing two electron beams.

Pierce [67], in March 1948, published an analysis which derived equations for increasing space-charge waves propagating in two electron beams containing ions, one beam having a zero or very low velocity, and he extended this in November 1949 [68]. In the meanwhile there was a great deal of activity, both in deriving theories and in experimental work, on what may be called, in general, double-beam tubes. Pierce and Hebenstreit [69], Hollenberg [70] and Pierce [71] published a series of papers on this subject and Haeff [72, 73] and Nergaard [74] were also active. These three groups of workers were working simultaneously and (apparently) quite independently and showed that practical double-beam tubes could be made to function.

Thus, in approximately one year, the foundations of efforts to produce increasing space-charge waves in double electron beams were laid. It is interesting to note that, for the second time, a large number of papers on the same topic were published within a few months, the first being in 1939 when the space-charge-wave theory was formulated. The work of each group will be considered in turn.

3.3.1. The work of Pierce and his group

In January 1949, Pierce and Hebenstreit [69] published a theoretical analysis which showed that if two beams of electrons having different average velocities (both in the same direction) where made to flow close to each other, then the charge densities or currents of the two beams interact, assuming that the charge densities or currents are large enough or the beams are close enough together. A consequence of this interaction is that it is possible for an increasing space-charge wave to be propagated along the system. The analysis is given below.

3.3.1.1. *The analysis*

The assumptions are:

(a) There is no electron motion normal to the direction of motion of the beam.

(b) Small signals only are considered.

(c) All quantities are constant across the cross-section of the beam.

(d) The electron velocity is much less than the velocity of light.

Note that all a.c. quantities are represented as $\exp\left[j(\omega t - \gamma z)\right]$ as before.

It is relevant to point out here, that Pierce and Hebenstreit made no reference to positive ion neutralization or to the cancelling out of the d.c. space-charge electric field or the d.c. tangential magnetic field; they merely assumed that these were cancelled out. Neither did they refer to the longitudinal d.c. magnetic field or any other mechanism for preventing radial electron motion; they again just simply assumed that there was no radial electron motion.

For one beam

$$v = -\frac{\eta \gamma V}{(\omega - \gamma u_0)} \qquad \text{(From Eqn 2.24)}$$

where V is the a.c. potential and

$$\rho = \frac{\rho_0 \gamma v}{(\omega - \gamma u_0)} \qquad \text{(Eqn 2.12)}$$

therefore
$$\rho = -\frac{J_0}{u_0}\frac{\gamma}{(\omega-\gamma u_0)^2}\eta\gamma V$$

therefore
$$\rho = -\frac{J_0}{u_0}\frac{\eta\gamma^2 V}{(\omega-\gamma u_0)^2}.$$

Putting in the suffices 1 and 2 for the first and second beam respectively gives

$$\rho_1 = -\frac{J_{01}}{u_{01}}\frac{\eta\gamma^2 V}{(\omega-\gamma u_{01})^2} \qquad 3.25$$

$$\rho_2 = -\frac{J_{02}}{u_{02}}\frac{\eta\gamma^2 V}{(\omega-\gamma u_{02})^2}. \qquad 3.25a$$

Let there be a fractional velocity separation u_s where

$$u_s = \frac{2(u_{01}-u_{02})}{(u_{01}+u_{02})} \qquad 3.26$$

and a mean velocity u_m where

$$u_m = \frac{2u_{01}u_{02}}{(u_{01}+u_{02})}. \qquad 3.27$$

Let V_m be a potential difference corresponding to the mean velocity u_m so that

$$u_m = \sqrt{(2\eta V_m)}. \qquad 3.28$$

Combining Eqns 3.26, 3.27 and putting $\gamma_0 = \omega/u_m$ gives

$$\omega/u_{01} = \gamma_0[1-(u_s/2)] \quad \text{and}$$
$$\omega/u_{02} = \gamma_0[1+(u_s/2)].$$

We now define a 'mean' current density J_m which together with u_m defines the ratios J_{01}/u_{01}^3 and J_{02}/u_{02}^3. Consider now the special case in which the electron guns have the same perveance:

$$J_{01}/u_{01}^3 = J_{02}/u_{02}^3 = J_m/u_m^3.$$

An alternative way of expressing this is that

$$J_{01}/V_{01}^{\frac{3}{2}} = J_{02}/V_{02}^{\frac{3}{2}} = J_{m}/V_{m}^{\frac{3}{2}}$$

If the total charge density ρ is given by $\rho_1 + \rho_2$ (note the assumption that d.c. values of charge density cancel out), then Eqns 3.25, 3.25a and 3.28 give

$$\rho_1 + \rho_2 = - \frac{J_{01}}{u_{01}} \frac{\eta\gamma^2 V}{(\omega - \gamma u_{01})^2} - \frac{J_{02}}{u_{02}} \frac{\eta\gamma^2 V}{(\omega - \gamma u_{02})^2}$$

and this reduces to

$$\rho = - \frac{J_{m}}{2u_{m}V_{m}} \gamma^2 \left\{ \frac{1}{\left[\gamma_0 \left(1 - \dfrac{u_s}{2} \right) - \gamma \right]^2} + \frac{1}{\left[\gamma_0 \left(1 + \dfrac{u_s}{2} \right) - \gamma \right]^2} \right\} V \quad 3.29$$

Note that the beams have been considered separately and the principle of conversation of charge applied to each separately.

Readers should not be confused by the negative sign in Eqn 3.29 which does not appear in the corresponding equation in Pierce and Hebenstreit's paper. This is because they put

$$\rho_{01} = (-J_{01})/u_{01} \quad \text{and} \quad \rho_{02} = (-J_{02})/u_{02}$$

thus assuming that the convection current density flows in the same direction as the electron beam since, for electrons, ρ_0 is negative. We have assumed that

$$\rho_{01} = (+J_{01})/u_{01} \quad \text{and} \quad \rho_{02} = (+J_{02})/u_{02}$$

to be consistent with our previous definition (Section 1.2.1) and this assumes that the convection current density flows in the opposite direction to the electron beam.

Eqn 3.29 is the ballistic equation giving the relationship between the a.c. charge density ρ produced by an impressed a.c. voltage V. A plot of this curve is shown in Figure 67. In order to find the propagation constant γ, the ballistic equation must be solved with a circuit equation which gives a relationship between the a.c. voltage V produced by the a.c. charge density ρ. To obtain this equation Pierce makes use of a device he frequently uses. He says that if γ is very small (the space-charge-wave wavelength is long compared with the tube radius and the electric fields are mainly transverse) one may write

$$\rho = C_1 V$$

where C_1 is a constant related to the capacitance per unit length of the region between the surface of the beam and the drift-tube wall. Con-

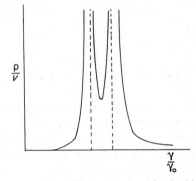

Figure 67. A plot of the ballistic equation of a double-beam system

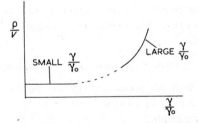

Figure 68. A plot of the circuit equation of a double-beam system

versely, if γ is large (λ is very short $-\lambda = 2\pi/\gamma$), Poisson's equation gives

$$\rho = \varepsilon_0 \gamma^2 V.$$

Hence for small γ, ρ/V is constant and as γ increases, ρ/V increases as γ^2. The curve is shown in Figure 68 and applies for a given value of ω

i.e. of γ_0. Figure 69 shows the curves representing the ballistic and circuit equations plotted on the same axis. The points of intersection are those at which solutions for both equations are found and the corresponding values of γ are those for which waves will propagate. Two curves for the ballistic equation are plotted each representing a different value of $J_m/(u_m V_m)$. Curve 1 has a larger value of $J_m/(u_m V_m)$ than curve 2, and it is

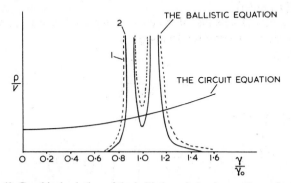

Figure 69. Graphical solution of the ballistic and circuit equations of a double-beam system

seen that as $J_m/(u_m V_m)$ increases the minimum value of ρ/V also increases. It is also seen that for the lower current case, curve 2, there are four intersections giving four real values of γ and hence four unattenuated waves. For the larger current case, curve 1, there are only two intersections giving two unattenuated waves. The two additional solutions to the ballistic and circuit equations are a pair of complex conjugates. They represent waves travelling at the same speed and with positive and negative attenuation constants.

It is possible to deduce, therefore, that as the current densities of the beams are increased a critical point is reached at which an increasing wave will propagate. Below that point four unattenuated waves only propagate. In other words, below the critical point the two beams behave as completely separate entities in an infinite longitudinal magnetic field. Above the critical point coupling between the beams occurs and results in the propagation of two unattenuated waves and a decreasing and an increasing wave. We return to this point in Section 3.3.4.3, but note the similarity with the mutual coupling between tuned circuits. In that case two resonant frequencies appear if the coupling is above a critical point.

Figure 69 also shows that the range of interest is around $(\gamma/\gamma_0) \simeq 1$ i.e. $\gamma \simeq \gamma_0$; the familiar condition. The two peaks converge to ∞ at $\gamma/\gamma_0 = [1 \pm (u_s/2)]$.

Let us now assume that at the point of interest, where $\gamma = \gamma_0$, we can say $\rho = d\varepsilon_0 \gamma^2 V$ where d is a factor > 1.

Putting

$$U^2 = \frac{-J_m}{2d\varepsilon_0 \gamma^2 u_m V_m}$$

Eqn 3.29 becomes

$$\frac{1}{\gamma^2 U^2} = \frac{1}{\left[\gamma_0\left(1 - \dfrac{u_s}{2}\right) - \gamma\right]^2} + \frac{1}{\left[\gamma_0\left(1 + \dfrac{u_s}{2}\right) - \gamma\right]^2} \qquad 3.30$$

and introducing the variable δ_2 where

$$\gamma = \gamma_0(1 + \delta_2) \qquad\qquad 3.31$$

Eqn 3.30 becomes

$$\frac{1}{U^2} = \frac{1}{\left(\delta_2 - \dfrac{u_s}{2}\right)^2} + \frac{1}{\left(\delta_2 + \dfrac{u_s}{2}\right)^2}. \qquad 3.32$$

This is a quadratic in δ_2 and gives

$$\delta_2 = \pm\left(\frac{u_s}{2}\right) \cdot \left\{\left(\frac{2U}{u_s}\right)^2 + 1 \pm \left(\frac{2U}{u_s}\right)\sqrt{\left[\left(\frac{2U}{u_s}\right)^2 + 4\right]}\right\}^{\frac{1}{2}}. \qquad 3.33$$

Eqns 3.31 and 3.33 show that if δ_2 is real, the waves are unattenuated, but if δ_2 is complex or imaginary then the waves have attenuation constants. Eqn 3.33 shows that in the case of the positive sign (in the brackets), δ_2 is real. For the negative sign δ_2 is real if

$$\left(\frac{2U}{u_s}\right)^2 + 1 > \left(\frac{2U}{u_s}\right)\sqrt{\left[\left(\frac{2U}{u_s}\right)^2 + 4\right]}$$

i.e. if
$$\left(\frac{U}{u_s}\right)^2 < \tfrac{1}{8}$$

If, however, $(U/u_s)^2 > \tfrac{1}{8}$, δ_2 is imaginary and we have a complex conjugate pair of propagation constants – a decreasing and an increasing wave. The relationship $(U/u_s)^2 > \tfrac{1}{8}$ is, therefore, the condition for gain to be obtainable in such a system and this gives a relationship between the 'mean' convection current density and the 'mean' d.c. velocity of the beams. As u_m decreases so J_m must increase to maintain the condition. Note that increasing U means increasing current density.

If U_{min} is the minimum value of U for which an increasing wave is obtained, $(U_{min}/u_s)^2 = \tfrac{1}{8}$. Eqn 3.33 gives, therefore, for an increasing wave,

$$\delta_2 = j\left(\frac{u_s}{2}\right)\left\{\left(\frac{2U}{u_s}\right).\sqrt{\left[\left(\frac{2U}{u_s}\right)^2 + 4\right]} - 1 - \left(\frac{2U}{u_s}\right)^2\right\}^{\frac{1}{2}}$$

and this becomes

$$\delta_2 = j\left(\frac{u_s}{2}\right)\left[\tfrac{1}{2}\left(\frac{U}{U_{min}}\right)^2\left\{\sqrt{\left(1 + 8\left(\frac{U_{min}}{U}\right)^2\right)} - 1\right\} - 1\right]^{\frac{1}{2}} \qquad 3.34$$

The gain $= 40\pi \log_{10} e \, |\delta_2| = 56 \cdot 4 |\delta_2|$. \qquad 3.35

Thus Eqns 3.34 and 3.35 permit the evaluation of the gain of the system and a curve of gain/(wavelength-unit u_s) is plotted *versus* $(U/U_{min})^2$ in Figure 70. Since U^2 is proportional to the current density, $(U/U_{min})^2$ is the ratio of the actual current density to that value which just gives an increasing wave. For large values of $(U/U_{min})^2$ the gain/(wavelength-unit u_s) approaches $27 \cdot 3$ dB.

This completes the simple theory given by Pierce and Hebenstreit and shows the possibility of being able to produce an increasing space-charge wave. These workers also gave a slightly more detailed analysis, taking boundary conditions into account.

One important factor not discussed as yet is that of the physical separation of the beams. This was left until a later paper by Pierce [71] and the importance of this parameter is indicated below.

Consider the case in which all the electrons in beam 1 are acted on by an a.c. potential V_1 and all electrons in beam 2 are acted upon by an a.c. potential V_2. We used the relationship $\rho = C_1 V$ earlier and we now have

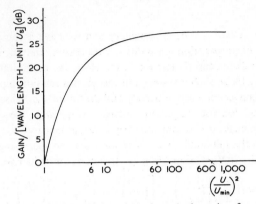

Figure 70. The effect of velocity separation on the gain of a double-beam system

(assuming the beams have equal effects on each other)

$$V_1 = C_1 \rho_1 + C_m \rho_2$$
$$V_2 = C_2 \rho_2 + C_m \rho_1$$

where C_1, C_2 and C_m are coefficients of induction. Eqns 3.25 and 3.25a now become

$$\rho_1 = -\frac{J_{01}\eta\gamma^2 V_1}{u_{01}(\omega - \gamma u_{01})^2} = A_1 V_1$$

and

$$\rho_2 = A_2 V_2 \,.$$

Therefore

$$V_1 = C_1 A_1 V_1 + C_m A_2 V_2$$
$$V_2 = C_2 A_2 V_2 + C_m A_1 V_1 \,.$$

Eliminating the potentials gives

$$(1 - A_1 C_1)(1 - A_2 C_2) = C_m^2 A_1 A_2 \,.$$

A similar procedure to that given earlier in this section gives

$$\frac{1}{\left(\delta_2 - \dfrac{u_s}{2}\right)^2} + \frac{1}{\left(\delta_2 + \dfrac{u_s}{2}\right)^2} = \frac{1}{L^2(1+\delta_2)^2}\left\{1 + \frac{L^4(1+\delta_2)^4\left(1 - \dfrac{C_m^2}{C_1 C_2}\right)}{\left(\delta_2 - \dfrac{u_s}{2}\right)^2\left(\delta_2 + \dfrac{u_s}{2}\right)^2}\right\}$$

3.36

having assumed, as before, that

$$\frac{\eta C_1 J_{01}}{u_{01}^3} = \frac{\eta C_2 J_{02}}{u_{02}^3} = \frac{\eta C_m J_m}{2u_m V_m} = L^2 .$$

On comparison with Eqn 3.32 one may put

$$\frac{1}{U'^2} = \frac{1}{L^2}\left[1 + \frac{L^4\left(1 - \dfrac{C_m^2}{C_1 C_2}\right)}{\left[\delta_2^2 - \left(\dfrac{u_s}{2}\right)^2\right]^2}\right]$$

3.37

so that Eqn 3.36 becomes

$$\frac{1}{\left(\delta_2 - \dfrac{u_s}{2}\right)^2} + \frac{1}{\left(\delta_2 + \dfrac{u_s}{2}\right)^2} = \frac{1}{U'^2} \qquad \text{if } \delta_2 \ll 1$$

and this is the same as Eqn 3.32. The solutions are given by Eqn 3.33 if we substitute U' for U. U' may be called the effective current. Substituting the value of δ_2 for the increasing wave [Eqn 3.34] and writing

$$\left(1 - \frac{C_m^2}{C_1 C_2}\right) = S^2 \quad \text{and} \quad \left(\frac{U'}{U'_{min}}\right)^2 = x .$$

Eqn 3.37 gives

$$\left(\frac{U'_{min}}{L}\right)^2 = \frac{1}{2x}\left\{1 + \left[1 - \frac{4S^2}{(\sqrt{1+\frac{8}{x}}-1)^2}\right]^{\frac{1}{2}}\right\}.$$

3.38

The condition $U'^2/u_s^2 > \frac{1}{8}$ applies and $(U'_{min}/u_s)^2 = \frac{1}{8}$; note that $\delta_2 \ll 1$ and γ is very close to γ_0. Eqn 3.38 is, therefore, a measure of the effect of the separation of the electron streams.

For infinitely remote electron beams $C_m = 0$ and therefore $S^2 = 1$. For coincident beams $C_m = C_1 = C_2$ and $S^2 = 0$

therefore
$$\left(\frac{U'_{min}}{L}\right)^2 = \frac{1}{x} = \left(\frac{U'_{min}}{U'}\right)^2 \qquad \text{(from Eqn 3.38)}$$

therefore
$$U' = L.$$

L can, therefore, be regarded as a critical current – the value of U' at $S^2 = 0$ (the beams are coincident).

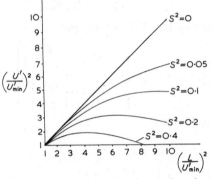

Figure 71. The effect of physical beam separation on the gain of a double-beam system

$(L/U'_{min})^2$ is, therefore, the ratio of this critical current to the minimum current for which there is gain. The variation of $(U'/U'_{min})^2$ versus $(L/U'_{min})^2$ for various values of S^2 is shown in Figure 71. When $S^2 \neq 0$ (the beams are separated) there is a maximum value of $(U'/U'_{min})^2$ when plotted against $(L/U'_{min})^2$. The maximum occurs when

$$1 - \frac{4S^2}{(\sqrt{1 + \frac{8}{x}} - 1)^2} = 0 \qquad \text{(from Eqn 3.38)}$$

i.e.
$$x_{max} = \frac{8}{[(1 + 2S)^2 - 1]}$$

and this occurs when $(L/U'_{min})^2 = 2x$.

As S^2 increases (the beams become further apart), so the maximum value of the effective current decreases. As $S^2 \rightarrow 1$ so $(U'/U'_{min})^2 \rightarrow 1$ (no gain) and $(L/U'_{min})^2 \rightarrow 2$.

The structure analyzed was that consisting of two coaxial tubular electron streams and Pierce stated that he 'treated this case and found that for such beams

$$S^2 = 1 - \frac{I_0(\gamma_0 a) K_0(\gamma_0 b)}{K_0(\gamma_0 a) I_0(\gamma_0 b)}$$

where a and b are the radii of the inner and outer beams respectively ...'
Pierce extended his analysis a little, taking the extreme case where $\gamma_0 a$ and $\gamma_0 b$ are sufficiently large so that the beams may be considered to be plane, and gave some curves showing the effect of physical beam separation in that special case.

3.3.1.2. *Design data*

It is not proposed to examine in detail all the material required for evaluating the gain of the increasing wave for a particular geometry of electron flow, as this is of little general interest. There is, however, one further point of interest.

If W^2 is defined as

$$W^2 = \omega_e^2/\omega^2$$

where ω_e is the electron plasma frequency associated with the mean space-charge density J_m/u_m

i.e.

$$\omega_e = \sqrt{(-J_m/\varepsilon_0 u_m)}$$

$$\frac{\omega_e^2}{\omega^2} = \frac{-J_m}{\varepsilon_0 u_m \omega^2} = W^2 .$$

Below a minimum value of W, called W_{min} there is no gain. W_{min} is a function of u_s the velocity separation and the ratio of the beam radius to the beam wavelength. It is assumed that the electron beams are 'intermingled' and that they have a radius b and the plasma wavelength is λ_0.

A detailed analysis shows that

$$8\left(\frac{W_{\min}}{u_{\rm s}}\right)^2 - 1 = \left\{\frac{K_1\left(2\pi\frac{b}{\lambda_0}\right)J_0\left(\sqrt{8\left(\frac{W_{\min}}{u_{\rm s}}\right)^2 - 1}\,.\,2\pi\frac{b}{\lambda_0}\right)}{K_0\left(2\pi\frac{b}{\lambda_0}\right)J_1\left(\sqrt{8\left(\frac{W_{\min}}{u_{\rm s}}\right)^2 - 1}\,.\,2\pi\frac{b}{\lambda_0}\right)}\right\}.$$

A plot of $(W_{\min}/u_{\rm s})^2$ *versus* b/λ_0 is shown in Figure 72. This shows that as the ratio of beam radius to wavelength, b/λ_0, increases so the critical

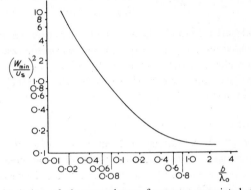

Figure 72. Variation of electron plasma frequency associated with 'mean' space-charge density

value of W, *i.e.* $W_{\min}$, the minimum value of W for which gain is obtainable, decreases; less current is required to obtain gain.

3.3.1.3. *Experimental work*

The practical work of this group was performed by Hollenberg [70] and published separately. He constructed two amplifiers. Both had an input helix and both had two identical probes, one at each end of the electron beams, for measuring the amplitude of the signal at each end of the beams. One amplifier had a helix output, the other had a 'gap' output. The distance between input and output was 22 cm. In both cases, the coaxial tubular electron beams were produced by two ring-shaped cathodes and passed through separate control grids. A common accelerating grid was used. The beams had a thickness of 0·76 mm in each case and were of 0·43 cm and 0·55 cm mean radii.

In the case of the amplifier with a helix output, a gain of 29 dB at 200 Mc/s was obtained with the inner beam potential at 54 V, the outer beam potential at 33 V and a current of 1·1 mA in each beam. Figure

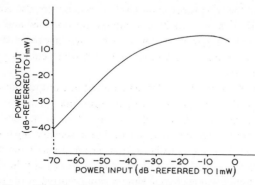

Figure 73. Gain of an experimental double-stream amplifier

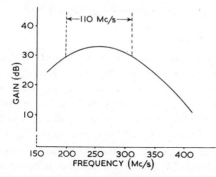

Figure 74. Bandwidth of an experimental double-stream amplifier

73 shows the output power *versus* input power. The gain is constant at 29 dB from low levels to an output power of 0·03 mW. At this point the gain drops. The variation of gain with frequency under the same conditions is shown in Figure 74 for the region in which the gain was constant; this is the linear part of the curve in Figure 73. The curve shows a

bandwidth of 110 Mc/s between 3 dB points. To ensure that the gain obtained was due to the double-stream interaction various experiments were performed. A comparison of the gain obtained with both beams on with the gain obtained with only one beam on was made. The signals obtained from the two probes in the electron beams were also compared. A gain of 1 dB with only the inner beam on was obtained and with the outer beam on a large loss was found, due to the fact that the velocity of the outer beam was far removed from that at which coupling with the input helix occurs.

In the case of the amplifier with 'gap' output, the output power was a little less than that for the first tube. Experiments on the gain of this amplifier as a function of the velocity separation of the beams were made. The theory predicts that, as the beam velocity separation increases from zero the gain increases from zero to a maximum and then starts to decrease as the velocity separation increases still further. The experiments found that such a maximum gain occurred at the predicted velocity separation.

The whole of this work is discussed in Section 3.3.4.

3.3.2. The work of Haeff

The first public announcement of this new method of amplifying signals of microwave frequencies was by Haeff [72]. A letter in *The Physical Review* in November 1948 discussed the method briefly and indicated the possible applications. It was here that the theory that solar noise could be due to the double-stream effect was first suggested. It appears that, in fact, Haeff had produced his theory earlier but was prevented from publishing it for security reasons. Full details of this analysis were published later [Haeff, 73] and since it is slightly different to the analysis of Pierce (Section 3.3.1.1) brief details of his method are given below.

3.3.2.1. *The analysis*

In exactly the same manner as Pierce, Haeff obtained Eqns 3.25 and 3.25a, which are:

$$\rho_1 = \frac{\varepsilon_0 \omega_{p1}^2 \gamma^2 V}{(\omega - \gamma u_{01})^2} \qquad 3.39$$

and
$$\rho_2 = \frac{\varepsilon_0 \omega_{p2}^2 \gamma^2 V}{(\omega - \gamma u_{02})^2} \qquad 3.40$$

where ω_{p1} and ω_{p2} are the plasma frequencies for beams 1 and 2 respectively, and u_{01} and u_{02} are d.c. velocities of the beams.

Now since
$$\nabla . \mathbf{D} = \rho$$
$$-\varepsilon_0 \frac{\partial^2 V}{\partial z^2} = \rho = \rho_1 + \rho_2$$

therefore
$$\varepsilon_0 \gamma^2 V = \rho_1 + \rho_2$$

therefore
$$\frac{\omega_{p1}^2}{(\omega - \gamma u_{01})^2} + \frac{\omega_{p2}^2}{(\omega - \gamma u_{02})^2} = 1 \qquad 3.41$$

Note that if $\omega_{p2} = 0$ Eqn 3.41 reduces to $1 = \omega_{p1}^2/(\omega - \gamma u_{01})^2$ and this is identical to Eqn 2.26 (Section 2.2.3) which leads to the simple unattenuated space-charge waves that propagate on an infinite beam. This is thus another way of deriving the results given in Section 2.2.3 in which the method of equating J/E was used. Note also that, as would be expected, Haeff made exactly the same assumptions as Pierce although he only mentioned the small-signal limitation. Neither mentioned the fact that they also assumed that the beam diameter was small compared to the diameter of the drift-tube, although Pierce introduced boundary conditions in his more detailed analysis.

Eqn 3.41 is the dispersion equation from which we can obtain γ, the propagation constant. In deriving this equation the conditions $\gamma = 0$ or $V = 0$, were excluded.

To solve Eqn 3.41 for the case when $u_{01} \neq u_{02}$ we assume
$$u_{01} = u_m + \delta_4 \qquad u_{02} = u_m - \delta_4$$

where $u_m =$ the mean velocity of the beam, as before [Eqn 3.27], and $\delta_4 = (u_{01} - u_{02})/2$ half the difference in velocity of the beams.

If
$$\gamma = (\omega/u_m) + \Gamma$$
$$(\omega - \gamma u_{01}) = \omega - \left(u_{01} \frac{\omega}{u_m} + u_{01} \Gamma \right) = -\frac{\delta_4 \omega}{u_m} - \Gamma u_{01}$$

and

$$(\omega - \gamma u_{02}) = \omega - \left(u_{02}\frac{\omega}{u_m} + u_{02}\Gamma\right) = +\frac{\delta_4\omega}{u_m} - \Gamma u_{02}.$$

Therefore Eqn 3.41 becomes

$$1 = \frac{\omega_{p1}^2}{\left(-\dfrac{\delta_4\omega}{u_m} - \Gamma u_{01}\right)^2} + \frac{\omega_{p2}^2}{\left(\dfrac{\delta_4\omega}{u_m} - \Gamma u_{02}\right)^2}.$$

If $\omega_{p1} = \omega_{p2}$

$$1 = \frac{1}{\left[\left(\dfrac{\delta_4\omega}{u_m\omega_{p1}}\right) - \left(\dfrac{\Gamma u_{02}}{\omega_{p1}}\right)\right]^2} + \frac{1}{\left[\left(\dfrac{\delta_4\omega}{u_m\omega_{p1}}\right) + \left(\dfrac{\Gamma u_{01}}{\omega_{p1}}\right)\right]^2}.$$

The solutions of this equations are

$$\frac{\Gamma u_m}{\omega_{p1}} = \pm\left\{\left(\frac{\delta_4\omega}{u_m\omega_{p1}}\right)^2 + 1 \pm \sqrt{\left[4\left(\frac{\delta_4\omega}{u_m\omega_{p1}}\right)^2 + 1\right]}\right\}^{\frac{1}{2}} \quad 3.42$$

The factor $(\delta_4\omega/u_m\omega_{p1})$ is dimensionless and expresses the degree of the difference in velocities of the electron beams — the inhomogeneity of the electron beams.

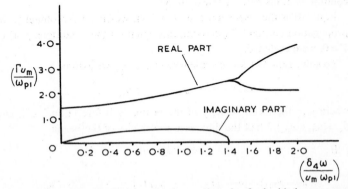

Figure 75. The effect of velocity separation on the gain of a double-beam system

The real and imaginary components of $(\Gamma u_m/\omega_{p1})$ are plotted in Figure 75 *versus* $(\delta_4\omega/u_m\omega_{p1})$. The imaginary component has finite values over a limited range of $(\delta_4\omega/u_m\omega_{p1})$ from 0 to $\sqrt{2}$ and it is only over this range that amplification can take place. This is simply seen from Eqn 3.42. The maximum value of the imaginary component equals $\frac{1}{2}$ when $(\delta_4\omega/u_m\omega_{p1})=\sqrt{3}/2$. These curves also indicate the variations of the real and imaginary components of γ with frequency, since $(\delta_4\omega/u_m\omega_{p1})$ is proportional to the signal frequency ω.

3.3.2.2. *Experimental work*

This group constructed an amplifier which had two cathodes and a common anode arranged so that the two (presumably cylindrical) beams were in close proximity to each other. Helicies were used to couple the

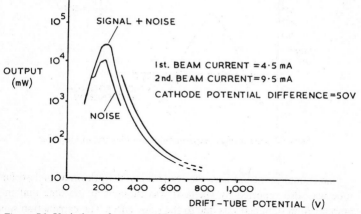

Figure 76. Variation of output with drift-tube potential of an experimental double-stream amplifier

signal to the beam. To obtain the optimum gain, the potentials between the two cathodes were adjusted: alternatively, one can adjust the drift-tube potential to give optimum gain. The experimental results obtained in a device with a 20 cm drift-tube are shown in Figure 76. No explanation of the curves was given.

A second double-stream amplifier was also constructed. The essential difference between this one and the first was that thorough mixing of the beams was arranged by having two spiral cathodes. Both were placed along the axis of the tube so that electrons emitted from the first cathode penetrated between the turns of the second spiral cathode. Figure 77 shows the results when a total current of 15 mA was used – the signal frequency was 3,000 Mc/s. It was stated that the loss at low and high cathode potential differences was due to 'mis-matching' but nevertheless a gain of 46 dB was obtained. The term mis-matching was not enlarged upon. A gain of 80 dB was estimated for the electronic gain. The bandwidth was measured and found to be over 30% at an estimated gain of 80 dB.

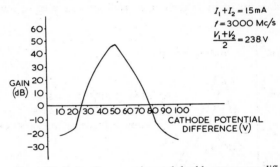

Figure 77. Gain of an experimental double-stream amplifier

One should point out here that experimental work on a single-beam tube was also reported by Haeff. It was thought at the time that the amplification obtained was due to the same effect. The explanation was that the inhomogeneity of the beam, causing the outer electrons to travel at a higher velocity than the inner electrons, caused the 'double-stream' increasing wave to be produced. The data given is insufficient to draw definite conclusions about this, but Bloom [58] discussed the matter in his memorandum and came to the conclusion that the effects Haeff observed could have been due to scalloped-beam amplification. It is now believed that for double-stream amplification there must be two peaks in the velocity distribution (Section 4.3) and this invalidates Haeff's conclusions that his results were due to double-stream interaction, unless of course his distribution had two peaks in it; this would have been fortuitous and not very likely. We return to this point in Section 4.3. Beam [75] suggested that the observed gain could be due to feedback by secondary electrons returning to the collector.

An alternative explanation may be that some form of klystron action was taking place. This was discussed in relation to his two-beam tubes, but was apparently overlooked when the single-beam tube was discussed.

3.3.3. The work of Nergaard

In December 1948 Nergaard [74], following a suggestion by C. W. Hansell, also published a theoretical analysis showing that it was possible to obtain increasing space-charge waves in a system containing two electron beams of different velocities. His analysis was mainly concerned with computing the gain/unit length of the tube, one of the most important parameters. Unfortunately, he used unrationalized c.g.s. units and some unusual symbols, which was rare for that period. However, he is the only worker not to ignore the d.c. space-charge effects. He did not attempt to explain a mechanism for cancelling them out and it is becoming increasingly evident that the mechanism is of no consequence; it is sufficient to say that d.c. space-charge effects are cancelled out or neglected, as did Nergaard. He also made it clear that the beams are assumed to be of infinite extent with arbitrary current densities and velocities, whereas the others left readers to deduce that this assumption was made.

There is little point in going through the analysis in detail, but it is interesting to look at the method of investigating the solutions of Eqn 3.41 for γ.

Using the divergence theorem and the equations of continuity and motion the dispersion equation, Eqn 3.41, was derived:

$$1 = \frac{\omega_{p1}^2}{(\omega - \gamma u_{01})^2} + \frac{\omega_{p2}^2}{(\omega - \gamma u_{02})^2}. \tag{3.41}$$

The detailed solution of this is pure algebra; it is simple and was given in an Appendix as was an investigation into the nature of the values of γ. It was found that the nature of the propagation could be discussed in terms of the following parameters:

$$l = \frac{\sqrt{(\omega_{p1}\omega_{p2})}}{\omega m'} \quad \text{where} \quad m' = \tfrac{1}{2}\left\{\sqrt{\left(\frac{u_{01}}{u_{02}}\right)} - \sqrt{\left(\frac{u_{02}}{u_{01}}\right)}\right\}$$

$$n = \sqrt{\left(\frac{\omega_{p1}u_{02}}{u_{01}\omega_{p2}}\right)}$$

and

$$\mu = \tfrac{2}{3}\left\{1 - \frac{l^2}{4}\left(n^2 + \frac{1}{n^2}\right)\right\}.$$

The results can be presented graphically. Figure 78a shows the minimum value of $l[=l_{min}]$ for which complex roots of the dispersion equation

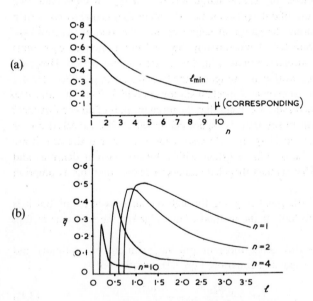

Figure 78. Gain of a double-beam system

exist. Plotted on the same axis are the corresponding values of μ. Alternatively one can plot a gain factor $\bar{q}$ *versus* l where

$$\bar{q} = \Gamma_i/l$$

and $\Gamma_i = \dfrac{\gamma_i\sqrt{(u_{01}u_{02})}}{n\omega}$, γ_i being the imaginary part of the propagation constant. Figure 78b shows this plot for parameter n.

Because the gain is proportional to $\bar{q}$ one can immediately visualise the variation of the gain with the parameters l and n. $\bar{q}$ has a maximum value of $\frac{1}{2}$ when $l = 2/\sqrt{3}$ and $n = 1$. As n increases so the gain falls off, slowly from the maximum in the direction of increasing l and sharply in the direction of decreasing l. The more n is removed from unity, the lower is the value of the maximum gain and the more rapidly the gain falls as l is removed from its optimum value.

To consider the bandwidth, a more useful curve is that of $\bar{q}$ *versus* $1/l$ because $\omega \propto 1/l$ and this is simply obtained from Figure 78b.

3.3.4. Discussion and comparison of the work of the three groups

It must be rare, to say the least, that three such historical groups of papers from separate teams of workers are published in such a short space of time. This is particularly so, because the concept was so novel. One wonders if these three groups were in contact with each other.

The method of producing increasing waves in the double-stream system is fundamentally different to that in any of the systems referred to in Section 3.2. In these systems, the increasing wave is obtained by the interaction of electrons in the beam with the charge on the surface of the wall of the drift-tube. In the travelling-wave tube, it is due to the interaction of the electrons with the fields produced by resonators, helices or other circuits. In the double-stream system, the increasing wave is due to interactions between the two beams and the drift-tube is of secondary importance. The important factors in the interaction are the electric field and the electrons themselves. The charge on the electrons produces the electric field and this stores energy and acts on the electrons. It was this phenomenon that led Pierce [15] to introduce his 'electro-mechanical wave' concept for space-charge waves (Section 2.2.5).

It is interesting to note here, that the author understands that Lord Rayleigh described similar interactions between two jets of water.

Of the three analyses, Haeff and Nergaard were effectively identical up to the stage of producing the dispersion equation

$$1 = \frac{\omega_{p1}^2}{(\omega - \gamma u_{01})^2} + \frac{\omega_{p2}^2}{(\omega - \gamma u_{02})^2} \qquad \text{(Eqn 3.41)}$$

and, within the limitations of the now familiar assumptions, mathematically rigorous. Pierce, on the other hand, derived the ballistic equation (Eqn 3.29) only after making the assumption $J_{01}/u_{01}^3 = J_{02}/u_{02}^3 = J_m/u_m^3$.

From this point onwards, the theories differ. Pierce makes the assumptions $\rho = C_1 V$ and $\rho = \varepsilon_0 \gamma^2 V$ depending on the magnitude of γ. Haeff, however, makes no such assumptions and uses the simplest of the three approaches. This was merely to introduce the average velocity of the electron beams u_m and δ_4, where $2\delta_4 = (u_{01} - u_{02})$ – the difference in velocities of the beams. He found later, that to solve the equation derived it was neccessary to assume that the plasma frequencies were equal, which placed a severe restriction on the results.

Nergaard was the only one to study in detail the factors on which γ depends, and although it is a matter of opinion, the author feels that his analysis gives the most useful general information. He did, however, use such phrases as 'this is shown to be', but gave no reference to the relevant analysis.

An advantage of the Haeff-Nergaard approach is that the dispersion equation can be solved graphically and this gives an insight into the physical mechanism by which the increasing space-charge wave is produced. The dispersion equation contains, on the right-hand side (R.H.S.), two terms each identical to Eqn 2.26, the dispersion equation for a single infinite beam confined to the z direction. Thus it is seen that, provided the two beams in the double-beam case can be considered as two separate entities, or, in other words, there is no coupling between the two beams, then the four solutions of the dispersion equation represent the two pairs of space-charge waves, one slow and one fast that propagate on each beam. Figure 79 shows the two separate dispersion curves and the unity line (L.H.S. of the dispersion equation). The four solutions are given by the intersection of the two curves. Suppose now the terms of the R.H.S., when plotted on the same axes, overlap as shown

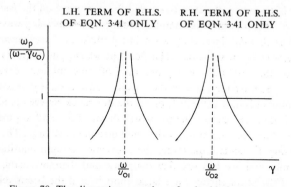

Figure 79. The dispersion equation of a double-beam system

in Figure 80. The resultant curve is that shown in dotted lines and it shows clearly that there is some 'interference' (coupling) between the two beams and that it is possible to reach a point when the unity line

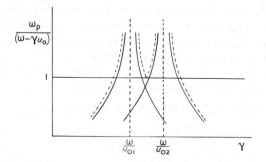

Figure 80. The dispersion equation of a double-beam system

does not intersect the curve in four places, but only in two places. In other words, we only have two unattenuated space-charge waves, one on each beam, in these circumstances. Since we assumed $u_{01} > u_{02}$ we see that the two unattenuated waves are the slow wave on the slow beam and the fast wave on the fast beam. The two waves that are coupled are the fast wave on the slow beam and the slow wave on the fast beam and at a certain point this coupling produces an increasing wave. It is also clear that the increasing wave has a phase velocity between the two electron beam velocities. The point at which gain is possible depends on the amplitude of the minimum of the combined curve. This depends on either the value of the plasma frequencies, if they are large the minimum is at a value > 1, or on the difference between ω/u_{01} and ω/u_{02}. If these are close together, which means if u_{01} and u_{02} are close together, then the minimum of the combined curve is large. The larger the plasma frequencies the larger the convection current densities.

Summarizing, we can say that coupling, and therefore, gain, is obtained if the beam currents are large enough or if the beam velocities are close together. Figure 69 is very similar to Figure 80, but the physical significance is not easily seen from Pierce's analysis. It is interesting to note that neither Haeff, Pierce nor Nergaard discussed the coupling in any detail, nor did they consider which of the four were the increasing and/or decreasing waves. The nature of this coupling could be that since the two electron beams are close to each other, there can be elastic collisions between fast electrons on the slow beam and slow electrons on the fast beam. Thus a slow interchange of energy between the two beams takes place so that, on the whole, the fast electrons are slowed down and the slow electrons are speeded up.

A fuller picture of the situation is obtained by taking the dispersion equation and performing the following operations:

(a) Put $\omega_{p1} = \omega_{p2}$ (this assumes that $\rho_{01} = \rho_{02}$)

(b) Put $\omega' = \left\{ \omega - \dfrac{\gamma(u_{01} + u_{02})}{2} \right\} \cdot \dfrac{1}{\omega_p}$

(c) Put $K = \dfrac{\gamma(u_{01} - u_{02})}{2} \cdot \dfrac{1}{\omega_p}$

Pure algebraic manipulation shows that the dispersion equation becomes

$$\frac{1}{(\omega'-K)^2} + \frac{1}{(\omega'+K)^2} = 1 \qquad 3.43$$

therefore $\qquad K = \pm\{(\omega'^2+1)\pm\sqrt{(4\omega'^2+1)}\}^{\frac{1}{2}}$

and K is complex if

$$\{(\omega'^2+1)\pm\sqrt{(4\omega'^2+1)}\} < 0$$

i.e. $\qquad\qquad$ if $\omega' < \sqrt{2}$ provided $\omega'^2 \neq 0$.

Thus for any value of ω' there are always four values of K and four waves.

$$\left.\begin{matrix}(a)\\(b)\end{matrix}\right\} = \pm\{(\omega'^2+1)+\sqrt{(4\omega'^2+1)}\}^{\frac{1}{2}}$$

$$\qquad\qquad\qquad\qquad\qquad\qquad\qquad\qquad 3.44$$

$$\left.\begin{matrix}(c)\\(d)\end{matrix}\right\} = \pm\{(\omega'^2+1)-\sqrt{(4\omega'^2+1)}\}^{\frac{1}{2}}$$

(a) and (b) are always real. (c) and (d) are also real unless $\omega' < \sqrt{2}$ in which case they are imaginary.

In summary, if $\omega' > \sqrt{2}$ all roots are real but if $\omega' < \sqrt{2}$ (a) and (b) are real and (c) and (d) are imaginary and an increasing wave propagates. The physical significance of this is shown in Figure 81. The actual waves indicate the coupling between the slow wave of the fast beam and the fast wave of the slow beam.

The gain obtained from the system is the sum of the gain due to each of the four constituent waves. If the values of γ_n are γ_1, γ_2, γ_3, γ_4, and assuming each wave is equally excited, the total electric field E is given by

$$E = E_{10}(e^{-j\gamma_1 z} + e^{-j\gamma_2 z} + e^{-j\gamma_3 z} + e^{-j\gamma_4 z}).$$

(If the total electric field at $z=0$ is E_{10}, each wave is initially $E_{10}/4$.) Two of these have complex propagation constants, $\gamma = -j\alpha + \beta$, and two do not. Since one of the two complex conjugates is a decreasing wave, we ignore it, but the other is an increasing wave, i.e. α is negative, and this increases exponentially as z increases.

The total effect is due, therefore, to three waves as shown in Figure 82.

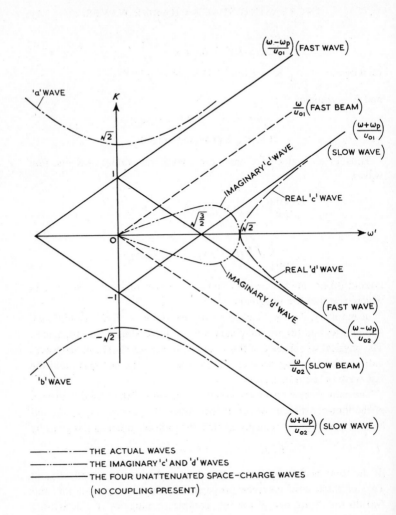

Figure 81. Illustration of the coupling between slow and fast space-charge waves

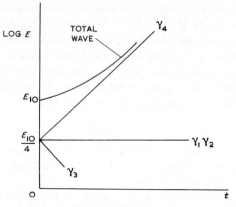

Figure 82. The total electric field due to the four space-charge waves in a double-beam system

The gain in dB $\qquad = 10 \log_{10}(P_{out}/P_{in})$

where P_{out} = power out and P_{in} = power in.

Therefore $\qquad \text{gain} = 10 \log_{10} \left| \dfrac{E_{out}}{E_{in}} \right|^2$

(assuming the input and output impedances are equal),

i.e. $\qquad G = 20 \log_{10} \left| \dfrac{E_{out}}{E_{in}} \right|$

and since the wave with γ_4 predominates

$$G = 20 \log_{10} \frac{E_{10}}{4E_{10}} e^{-\alpha_4 z}$$

$$= 20 \log_{10} \tfrac{1}{4} - \alpha_4 \, z \log_{10} e$$

therefore $\qquad G = -12 - 54 \cdot 6 gN = A - 54 \cdot 6 gN$.

$g = -\alpha_4 \lambda / 2\pi$ the gain parameter.

$N = z/\lambda$ the number density (the number of wavelengths in distance z).

A = initial loss.

Note that the gain varies with λ i.e. with frequency.

We are now in a position to compare the double-beam tube with other types of tube. If γ_n ($n = 1, 2, 3, 4$) are all real, which means there is no coupling, the tube behaves like a velocity-modulation tube of rather greater complexity than the usual tube. If two values of γ_n are real and the other two are zero, there is no increasing wave and the tube behaves like a conventional velocity-modulation tube [Hahn and Metcalf, 5]. Eqns 3.44 show that the condition for this is that

$$\omega' = \sqrt{2}$$

This is $K = 0$ for waves (c) and (d) and amounts to $u_{01} = u_{02}$, the beams having the same velocity. (This applies only to the case of $\rho_{01} = \rho_{02}$ as assumed in deriving Eqn 3.44.)

Finally, if one or more γ_n are complex, it is possible to have an increasing wave. It happens that if one γ_n is complex another is conjugate to it and a decreasing wave is obtained as well.

The double-stream amplifier has several advantages over other devices. No field supporting or wave guide structures are required. Although the two beams have to be close to each other, and this presents some problems, they do not have to be near to a drift-tube. Also, a long electron flow between input and output circuits is possible and difficulties of keeping the beam in synchronism with a circuit wave do not arise. The forward motion of both beams suggests that a backward circuit wave is unlikely, thus eliminating the need of attenuation circuits now used in travelling-wave tubes. The synchronizing of the beams may be a problem however, and it is possible that secondary electrons may give rise to backward waves.

Unfortunately, the experimental work performed by these groups was not reported in any detail and it is not possible to give a reasoned conclusion. One can say, however, that Hollenberg's experiments appear to show double-stream amplification, but that Haeff's single-beam tube action is definitely suspect.

Some theoretical calculations by Nergaard showed that if optimum conditions exist, i.e. $l = 2/\sqrt{3}$, $n = 1$:

(a) If the current density of one beam $= 0.050$ A/cm^2

beam voltage	= 1,600 V
frequency	= 3,000 Mc/s

$$\left\{ I_2 = I_1 \left(\frac{V_2}{V_1} \right)^{\frac{3}{2}} = 0 \cdot 022 \ \text{A/cm}^2 \right\}$$

the gain $G = 1,340 \sqrt{\left/ \left(\frac{I_1}{V_1^{\frac{3}{2}}} \right) \right.} = 0 \cdot 84 \quad \text{dB/cm}.$

(b) If the current density of one beam = $0 \cdot 1$ A/cm^2

beam voltage	= 500 V
frequency	= 3,000 Mc/s
	$G = 4 \cdot 0$ dB/cm.

(Details of the calculations were not given.)

A travelling-wave tube operating under the same conditions as in (a) above showed a gain of $1 \cdot 14$ dB/cm.

Thus one would expect a double-beam tube operating under conditions as in (b) to give a power gain that would be of practical use, but one should remember that this is an ideal model and practical gains would be less than those calculated.

Once again we have the apparently curious lack of further practical work on a device that appears to be a reasonable practical proposition. It may well be that difficulties of exciting the space-charge waves are the limiting factors. It is easy to show theoretically that waves may propagate 'if they are excited', which is the operative phrase, but is it easy to excite them? The literature is sparse, particularly on experimental work and the difficulties encountered rarely referred to. Consequently it is a matter of conjecture why little further experimental work has been reported. Since the most serious obstacle to the extension of the h.f. limit of tube operation is the need to use wave guide structures, it is reasonable to assume that the problems involved in exciting the increasing waves are as great as those associated with the wave guide structures in other types of tube and such as to make further experimental work unjustifiable. However, we are mainly concerned with the theoretical aspects of space-charge-wave theory and the double-stream interaction is an extremely interesting phenomenon. The following sections are devoted to a study of the latest publications on this subject. Before proceeding, we should just note that Pierce [67], before publishing his classical work with Hebenstreit, showed that two special, similar, increasing waves can be obtained in a system in which there are two beams of charged particles having different velocities, one of which has a zero or very low velocity. It was shown that if the beam was confined by a magnetic field, there was an increasing wave near the ion plasma frequency and another near the ion cyclotron frequency (usually around $5 \cdot 5 \times 10^6$ c/s and 10^4 c/s respectively). Pierce [68], later investigated the nature of increasing waves for a wide range of parameters, including the range from ion noise to that of double-stream amplification, but obtained no further information about the rather special increasing waves associated with the ion plasma and ion cyclotron frequencies. There was a brief reference to the case in which the beams travelled in the opposite directions. Lopukhin and Roshal [76] discussed this in more detail, considering the increasing waves for various values of some parameters such as beam separation and current density.

3.3.5. The latest developments

Most of the work on the subject of double-stream interactions published since 1949 has been devoted to discussing the original analyses given in Sections 3.3.1, 3.3.2 and 3.3.3. Indeed, Vural [77] in 1961 was the first to make an entirely new contribution to the development of the subject and his is the latest contribution to the author's knowledge.

Feinstein and Sen [78] criticized the analysis of Haeff (and the others by implication) on the grounds that it was not rigorous enough, but their more rigorous analysis was mainly concerned with the case of a beam moving into a stationary plasma; similar to Pierce [67]. This opens up a vast sphere of activity, both theoretical and experimental, for it leads naturally to a study of plasmas or slightly ionized gases, a subject closely related to that under discussion. Space does not permit the pursuit of this subject, but a link is provided by Yadavalli [79], who adopted Pierce's [67] analysis to treat the problem of an electron beam traversing a plasma from the point of view of double-stream-amplifier theory (amongst other approaches).

The real issue, however, was raised by Piddington [80], [81] in 1956 and pursued by him in 1958 [Piddington, 82]. This is whether or not the amplification shown theoretically, and purported to have been demonstrated experimentally, was 'true' amplification or whether the wave apparently increasing in one direction is in fact one decreasing in the reverse direction. As mentioned in Section 3.1 we are here only concerned with growth in space and have always considered the real and imaginary parts of γ as derived from the dispersion equation. It is possible to have either

    (a) Growth in space, which requires a real ω but an imaginary part of γ; real ω means that the driving frequency is fixed, or

    (b) Growth in time, which requires a real γ, but an imaginary part of ω.

Case (b) is of particular interest to plasma physicists and for our purposes a growth in time is merely an instability.

Case (a) is the type of growth required in microwave electronics work, because it is 'true' amplification and this is required in electronics devices.

It is not proposed to enter into an involved discussion of the details of the controversy or to discuss growing waves or the solution of the dispersion equation. There is a wealth of literature on the subject, much of it inspired by Piddington's suggestion that the theories of Haeff, Nergaard, Pierce and Hebenstreit and Feinstein and Sen are untenable. A paper, quoting many references on the subject of growing waves in general, is given by Sturrock [83], although Pierce and Walker [84] made some very pertinent remarks. In 1960, Swift-Hook [85], dealing in particular with double-stream interactions and Piddington's work, finally settled the issue beyond reasonable doubt. Using a condition for 'true' amplification derived by Buneman [86, 87], he showed theoretically that the apparent growth in space obtained by the pioneers did represent 'true' growth and that double-stream amplification is possible. Nevertheless, the work of Piddington, who claimed that the other analyses did not show 'true' amplification, demonstrated that it is very easy to confuse waves increasing in space with waves increasing in time (evanescent) and this led to a very useful discussion and clarification of the growth of waves.

The theory of travelling-wave interaction between an electron beam and a nearly synchronous r.f. wave, is so similar to the theory of double-stream interaction (certainly so far as the solution of the dispersion equation and the increasing wave are concerned) that if one theory were proved untenable, the other would be suspect. Although there is hardly any other experimental work on the double-stream amplifier alone (just as little experimental work was carried out with the sole purpose of verifying space-charge-wave theory), the wealth of experimental evidence that the travelling-wave interaction is as predicted theoretically, is in any case sufficient evidence for one to conclude that 'true' amplification is obtainable in double-stream interactions. Despite the fallacious experimental evidence of part of Haeff's work, the other experimental evidence reported in Sections 3.3.1 and 3.3.2 supports the conclusion.

Finally, at the beginning of this section, reference was made to a recent paper by Vural [77]; we will now discuss this briefly.

The obvious next step is to consider the double-stream interactions in the presence of a finite d.c. longitudinal magnetic field, as opposed to an infinite d.c. longitudinal magnetic field, and this Vural did. Unfortunately, one immediately becomes involved in cyclotron waves which are outside the scope of this monograph. Davies [88] gives a good introduction to these waves. It is equally unfortunate that Vural's work is based on an analysis for a stationary plasma, another subject we are unable to investigate. He states that the plasma analysis is simpler and the fact that the propagation constants do not greatly differ from those of an electron beam enables one to use this analysis for the case of two electron beams. To support this assumption, he produces an equation for p^2, the square of the plasma frequency reduction factor, for the case of a single beam (taken as a special case) and shows that curves of his value of p versus γb do not differ greatly from those given by Pashke (Figures 25–27). His equation for p^2 differs slightly from our Eqn 2.63 (Section 2.4.5.1) however, although its form is identical, and the information provided in the paper is limited to such an extent that one would have to perform a detailed investigation of the plasma physics literature before being able to compare the two different approaches and account for the slight discrepancy.

Nevertheless, it is worth while to introduce a diagram, similar to

that of Figure 81, for the general case of two beams flowing in a finite
d.c. longitudinal magnetic field (Figure 83). This was derived by the
theory of coupled modes [Louisell, 89] as was Figure 81. The principle
of the theory is that a system is divided into a number of smaller systems,
such as a beam and a circuit or two separate beams, where propagation

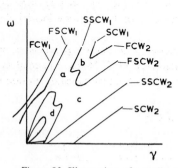

FCW – Fast Cyclotron Wave
FSCW – Fast Space-Charge Wave
SCW – Slow Cyclotron Wave
SSCW – Slow Space-Charge Wave
Suffix 1 – Faster Electron Beam
Suffix 2 – Slower Electron Beam

Figure 83. Illustration of coupling between slow and fast waves

characteristics can be deduced separately when no coupling exists.
When coupling is introduced, interaction occurs if the field distributions
of the separate smaller systems are similar. The phase velocities of the
separate, smaller systems have to be nearly the same. Figure 83 shows
that one effect of reducing the strength of the magnetic field is to permit
the possibility of coupling between the cyclotron and space-charge
waves and also between the cyclotron waves alone; this is in addition
to the coupling between space-charge waves alone as was the case
previously when cyclotron waves did not exist.

The possible interactions are:

(a) The fast cyclotron wave of the slow beam with the slow space-
    charge wave of the fast beam.

(b) The fast cyclotron wave of the slow beam with the slow cyclotron
    wave of the fast beam.

(c) The fast space-charge wave of the slow beam with the slow cyclotron wave of the fast beam, and

(d) The fast space-charge wave of the slow beam with the slow space-charge wave of the fast beam.

Two detailed diagrams of special cases as calculated on a computer were given. These were for when (1) $u_{01}/u_{02} = 0.8$ and (2) $u_{01}/u_{02} = 0.5$ and showed that in case (1) all four possible interactions can take place, but that in case (2) the interaction between the space-charge waves does not occur. This indicates the critical effect of the ratio of velocities of the beam.

It is possible to conclude, therefore, that several practical devices may be possible. These are tabulated in Table 2. No experimental work has been reported, but the results Vural obtained indicate that double-

Table 2

FAST CYCLOTRON WAVE SLOW BEAM	SLOW CYCLOTRON WAVE FAST BEAM	CYCLOTRON WAVE D.S.A.
FAST CYCLOTRON WAVE SLOW BEAM	SLOW SPACE-CHARGE WAVE FAST BEAM	CYCLOTRON, SPACE-CHARGE WAVE D.S.A.
FAST SPACE-CHARGE WAVE SLOW BEAM	SLOW CYCLOTRON WAVE FAST BEAM	CYCLOTRON, SPACE-CHARGE WAVE D.S.A.
FAST SPACE-CHARGE WAVE SLOW BEAM	SLOW SPACE-CHARGE WAVE FAST BEAM	SPACE-CHARGE WAVE D.S.A.

stream devices based on the predictions of his work could have promising characteristics. This is particularly so of the wide-band frequency response, and there is reason to believe that further experimental work on double-stream devices would be fruitful, although Vural himself did not indicate that any such work is being, or will be, carried out in his organisation.

3.4 FINAL COMMENTS

On commencing to read this chapter, one might have felt that we were about to discuss some work that has a considerable influence on many practical devices now in constant use throughout the world. In the event, however, our discussion has been on what must now be regarded as some purely academic investigations. Having carefully studied the literature, it is clear to the author that devices that depend on the increasing space-charge wave alone for their operation are not widely used today. The travelling-wave tube obviously has a superior performance. However, some recent theoretical work by Vural [77] indicates that there may be something to be gained by investigating the possibilities of double-stream interactions in finite d.c. magnetic fields; something not previously attempted.

The work on double-stream interactions enables us to introduce an important concept not previously discussed. Readers will have observed that the coupling between waves, cyclotron or space-charge, that produces increasing waves, is always between a fast wave and a slow wave. The reason for this is connected with the power flow along an electron beam. Power flows associated with slow waves on a beam are negative, whereas power flows associated with fast waves are positive. Thus, it is possible to remove energy from a beam by increasing the amplitude of the slow wave; conversely, supplying energy to the beam increases the amplitude of the fast wave. Thus, when coupling between a fast wave and a slow wave takes place, there can be an interchange of energy between them. The slow wave can deliver energy to the fast wave, the slow wave energy becomes more negative and its amplitude is increased. The fast wave is similarly decreased in amplitude, and we now see why we always get a conjugate pair of complex propagation constants in the analysis for double-stream interactions, giving both an increasing and a decreasing wave simultaneously. Power flow is discussed in Chapter 5.

In conclusion, this chapter could have included a section on increasing space-charge waves on multiple electron beams. Haeff [90] investigated this in a discussion on the origin of solar noise and showed that the dispersion equation is

$$\sum_{1}^{n} \frac{\omega_{pn}^2}{(\omega - \gamma u_{0n})^2} = 1$$

(for an infinite d.c. magnetic field) as would be expected if n discrete beams are considered in exactly the same way as in Section 3.3.2. Parzen [91] also discussed the general case but took the special case of two beams in order to reduce the equations to a form that is soluble. However, this is of little practical interest in microwave electronics work although Haeff's paper is interesting. The mechanism could play an important part in many natural phenomena such as abnormally intense bursts of solar noise associated with sun spot activity. To microwave engineers, the spread of d.c. velocities in a single electron beam is of greater interest. The effects of a beam having a multiplicity of d.c. velocities rather than a constant d.c. velocity u_0 is discussed in Chapter 4.

CHAPTER 4

The Propagation of Space-Charge Waves on Multi-Velocity Beams

4.1 GENERAL REMARKS

Probably the most significant effect in practical beams that we have ignored in the previous chapters is the fact that all electrons at any one plane z_a do not have the same d.c. velocity u_0, but there is a velocity distribution. Many of the other restrictions placed on the theory can be applied in practice but it is impossible to produce a true mono-velocity beam. This chapter, therefore, is devoted to a discussion of the effects the velocity distribution has on the propagation of the space-charge waves.

In view of the practical significance of the mono-velocity restriction, one would expect there to be a large amount of literature on this subject, especially in recent years, and particularly in respect of the devices now in general use. In fact, this is not so; there is comparatively little published work on this subject and the chief reason may well be that it is difficult to know the type of distribution that one obtains in practice. Most of those workers that have ventured into this field have concerned themselves with trying to find a velocity distribution that gives results that could account for some experimentally observed phenomena, particularly noise phenomena. Consequently, the literature is very varied and does not follow any particular pattern as hitherto; it is a conglomeration of attempts to find a suitable framework within which to work and the situation is still very fluid.

Another difficulty is that some very complicated mathematical techniques have to be used and computers are required to solve many of the equations obtained in the analyses. As we are mainly concerned with the effects of multi-velocity beams on our earlier theories, it is not intended to derive mathematically the results obtained by the various workers in this field: adequate references are given for readers interested in the detailed mathematics. We merely set out briefly the procedures used and indicate the results obtained, particularly with reference to those results that have a bearing on the work of Chapters 2 and 3.

4.2 THE FIRST ATTEMPT TO CONSIDER THE EFFECT OF VELOCITY DISTRIBUTION

The effect of thermal velocity spread on noise and signals on electron beams was studied by MacDonald [92], but he ignored the effects of space-charge. The first attempt to investigate the effect of velocity distribution when space-charge forces are also considered was made by Watkins [93] in 1952.

He made the following assumptions:

(a) Motion is confined to the z direction.

(b) Small signals only are considered.

(c) The d.c. space-charge of the beam is neutralized.

(d) The d.c. velocity distribution is half-Maxwellian (as used by Rack, [94]).

Note that the half-Maxwellian distribution ensures that only one velocity is associated with each group of electrons.

The basis of the analysis is the Liouville theorem of statistical mechanics (Goldstein, [95], Lindsay, [96]), which is part of a ballistic theory. The theorem states that the total derivative of the density function in phase space is zero. A general analysis, in which it is shown that space-charge is the most important factor in determining the behaviour of noise currents in electron streams at high frequencies, velocity spread playing a comparatively minor role, is followed by the treatment of a special case that is of particular interest to us. This is the case of a drifting beam with a small-signal velocity modulation. The equations derived indicate that a standing wave of convection current density is obtained, and if limiting conditions are applied the equations give the results for a mono-velocity beam. The first order effect of the multi-velocity beam is to reduce the amplitude of the standing wave, and to lengthen the electronic wavelength. A second order effect is that the phase of the a.c. convection current density is altered.

Another special case studied is that of a drifting beam with full shot noise (caused by the random emission of electrons) in each velocity class at the input. This showed that the standing wave of noise current had minima along the beam as found experimentally by Cutler and Quate [41]. In Section 2.5.2 their work was discussed and Figure 28 clearly shows these minima. Although we do not stress the point in Section 2.5.2, the theory of Chapter 2 indicated that these minima should have been zero; we now see that this is not so. Watkins also showed that the value of the first minimum after the modulating grids increases as the square of the frequency and also with increasing velocity spread.

4.3 THE DEVELOPMENT OF THE THEORY

In January 1954 Kent [97] published a paper, the chief function of which was to see if inhomogeneity of the unneutralized beam, caused by the potential at the centre of the beam being depressed by the space-charge thereby causing the velocity at the centre of the beam to be less than the velocity at the edges, could account for the experimental results Haeff [73] obtained with his single-beam tube. Haeff thought he observed gain and attributed this to double-stream interaction between different velocity streams within the inhomogenous beam (Section 3.3.2.2). Kent also briefly considered an analogy of the velocity distributed beam. He showed that in the case of a sheet beam, assuming the inhomogeneity is small, increasing waves on a single beam are not possible. The analogy with the velocity distributed beam showed that increasing space-charge waves cannot exist unless the distribution function has more than one maxima. He pointed out that if an inhomogenous beam could support increasing waves, one could expect that beam noise would grow exponentially, something not found in practice. Thus, there is considerable practical evidence that single electron beams, by themselves, cannot support increasing waves although such evidence is admittedly negative. Unfortunately, Kent's mathematical methods are not given in detail and he frequently mentions techniques and names without giving references. It is impossible, therefore, to discuss his work in more detail without carrying out a detailed investigation of his mathematical procedures.

Later that year, Yadavalli [98] also published a paper on the effects of velocity distribution, and his analysis was based on the Liouville theorem, as was Watkins' [93]. He obtained an integral equation and solved it by using Laplace transforms [99], his solutions being specifically for the small-signal, velocity modulated drifting beam and for a beam initially possessing full short noise in each velocity class. This is very similar to Watkins (Section 4.2), but Yadavalli assumes a rectangular distribution instead of a half-Maxwellian distribution (which again ensures that only one velocity is associated with each group of electrons). It is shown, by comparison of equations for the a.c. convection current density in the two cases, that for the drifting electron beam with small-signal velocity modulation the same results are obtained in both cases, except that the rectangular distribution gives a slightly smaller current standing wave amplitude than the half-Maxwellian distribution. Yadavalli, in an appendix, attempted to justify the use of the rectangular distribution.

In November 1954 Watkins and Rynn [100] applied the analysis Watkins gave in 1952 to the one dimensional model of the travelling-wave tube, to investigate the effect of velocity distribution on travelling-wave tube performance. For small velocity spreads, thermal velocities were found to reduce the gain of the device by less than one part in 10^4.

G. A. Gray [101] in 1960 and Carrol [102] in 1963, applied their analyses to the travelling-wave tube and obtained results in agreement with Watkins and Rynn. G. Gray used the concept of a single velocity equivalent of the velocity distribution, following the work of F. Gray [103]. Details of the analyses are given in those three papers which have to be read in conjunction.

G. Gray found that to the first order, space-charge wave propagation on a beam with a distribution of velocities can be described by the usual single velocity theory if one uses u_0, the d.c. part of the average beam velocity and a plasma frequency reduction factor R^1 where

$$R^1 = \left[\left(\frac{\omega_q}{\omega_p} \right)^2 + S^1 \right]^{\frac{1}{2}}$$

$$S^1 = \frac{\int_{-\infty}^{+\infty} n_1 (v - u_0)^2 \, dv}{u_0^2 \left(\frac{\omega_p}{v}\right)^2 \int_{-\infty}^{+\infty} n_1 \, dv}$$

$n \, dv$ = mass density of particles with velocities
lying between v and $v + dv$

and $\qquad n = n_0 + n_1 \, e^{j\omega t}$

This is assuming a half-Maxwellian distribution. The analysis gives the equation for the a.c. convection current density that Watkins and Rynn obtained. For small velocity spreads, S^1 can be ignored and R^1 equals the plasma frequency reduction factor for a mono-velocity beam. Gray also studied the double-stream amplifier and, using his single-beam equivalent, obtained the same determinantal equation as Pierce obtained.

Carrol used a different method of analysing the multi-velocity beam. G. Gray and Watkins used the velocity distribution function, but Carrol points out that in applications of more than one dimension the method is difficult to deal with. Their method is therefore not used, and the velocity distribution is replaced by two concepts. Firstly, an average velocity (a concept also used by G. Gray), and secondly, a tensor temperature. The detailed mathematical analysis is given in the paper, and when applied to the travelling-wave tube, equations are obtained that agree with some obtained by Gray and Watkins and Rynn.

In approximately 1960, Siegman [104] published an internal memorandum in which he considered propagation on a drifting electron beam with a square velocity distribution, referred to an energy co-ordinate. He replaced the velocity co-ordinate with the energy co-ordinate and made a small-signal density function analysis. This shows that there are three waves on the system now instead of the two waves found in the mono-velocity theory. These are the usual fast and slow unattenuated waves plus a fast unattenuated wave in the opposite direction. Prior to this, Siegman [105] published a paper setting out some of the mathematical procedures which assist in the density function type analysis.

He too showed that such an analysis becomes equivalent to the mono-velocity analysis if the velocity spread is small compared with the mean d.c. velocity of the beam. If the velocity spread is large, no simple transmission-line type of theory can be applied to the beam.

Finally, Berghammer [106] suggested that if one considers a Max-wellian distribution of velocities, the fast space-charge wave of the mono-velocity theory is replaced by a fast wave packet which decays with distance because of phase mixing, so that only the slow space-charge wave propagates for any distance. He showed that the a.c. current-modulation standing wave has the form of a damped sinusoid, with finite minima, and at large distances from the modulating device the current modulation approaches a constant level.

4.4 THE EXPERIMENTAL WORK

Mihran [107] studied the signal as a function of the width of the d.c. velocity distribution function *versus* the space-charge wavelength. In practice, the d.c. velocity spreads used are of the order of 10%, and the r.f. current was studied over a distance equivalent to about 20 r.f. cycles.

4.4.1. The apparatus

The experimental apparatus is very similar to that which Mihran used in his investigations of scalloped-beam amplification (Figure 48), and

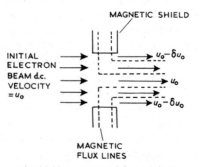

Figure 84. Gun-magnetic shield system used for producing a velocity distribution

he here uses his fine wire probe method to measure the beam diameter. The 'gun' system is exactly the same in both cases. The beam is confined by a longitudinal d.c. magnetic field which was variable from 2 to 10 times the Brillouin value, which was 33 gauss assuming the beam diameter was the same as the cathode diameter. The injection system is such that there is a spread in the axial velocities of the electrons across a radius. Figure 84 shows the gun-shield system and the fact that the centre electron is at full beam velocity, whereas the outer electrons have reduced axial velocities since they cross a radial magnetic field. (They thus receive rational energy and therefore lose some of their axial velocity). In practice, the beam is scalloped, but Mihran assumes that the degree of scalloping is so slight that it does not play a part in the phenomenon observed. One should note, however, that this could, at least partially, account for any discrepancy between experiment and theory, particularly at low longitudinal magnetic field strengths.

4.4.2. The results

Figure 85 is a plot of the r.f. power *versus* distance along the beam with d.c. magnetic field strength as parameter. The signal applied was at 1,000 Mc/s. It is seen that as the d.c. magnetic field strength changes from 128 to 192 gauss (which is from 4 to 6 times the Brillouin field) the pattern of the r.f. power changes from the familiar space-charge wave behaviour to one in which the standing wave pattern is highly damped. It was suggested that this was due to the increased velocity spread caused by the increasing field. Figure 86 shows a similar behaviour. Here, the magnetic field strength (and thus the velocity spread) was constant at 160 gauss (5 times the Brillouin field) and the d.c. beam current is used as a parameter. This graph is, therefore, one of r.f. current behaviour in a beam with constant velocity spread.

4.4.3. Comparison with theory

Siegman [104] derived an expression for the current resulting from excitation by a circuit current in a single velocity class. Mihran [107] took this expression and integrated it to allow for current excitation in all velocity classes, assuming that the square of the ratio of excess d.c.

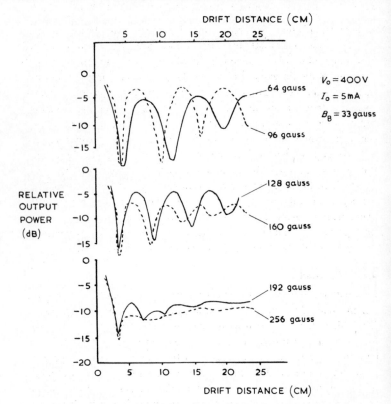

Figure 85. Variation of signal output power on a multi-velocity beam

velocity to average d.c. velocity is small compared to unity. The theoretical curve he obtained is shown in Figure 87 and plotted on the same axes are the experimental results, the beam current for both the theoretical and experimental curves being equal to 2·5 mA. It is seen that beyond the first maximum there is considerable disagreement between the theoretical and experimental results, for the amplitude of the third maximum is not greater than the amplitude of the second maximum as predicted theoretically.

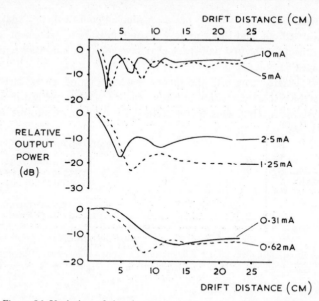

Figure 86. Variation of signal output power on a multi-velocity beam

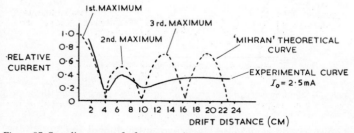

Figure 87. Standing wave of r.f. current along a multi-velocity beam (theoretical and experimental)

Mihran concluded, therefore, that the one-dimensional linearized distribution analysis cannot be used to predict the behaviour of the r.f. current found in his experimental apparatus and one must, therefore, question the validity of this type of analysis when applied to noise phenomena on multi-velocity beams. A simpler 'ballistic theory' analysis was carried out, and this also gave a good measure of agreement with experiment for the first half-space-charge wavelength, but disagreement beyond that point.

The disagreement with the theory is disappointing, particularly as this is the first direct attempt to verify a theory based on the distribution analysis approach. One is, therefore, inclined to enquire if another velo-

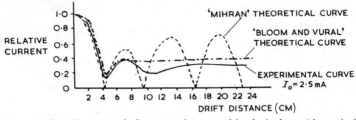

Figure 88. Standing wave of r.f. current along a multi-velocity beam (theoretical and experimental)

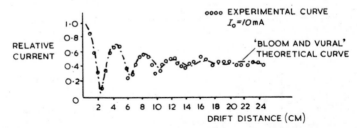

Figure 89. Standing wave of r.f. current along a multi-velocity beam (theoretical and experimental)

city distribution would give better agreement. Bloom and Vural [108] looked into the matter in 1963. They carried out Yadavalli's [98] analysis, but assumed a half-Maxwellian distribution instead of a rectangular distribution. The results of this analysis (also a one-dimensional linearized distribution analysis) were compared with the experimental results of Mihran for two values of beam current, 2·5 mA and 10 mA: these are plotted in Figures 88 and 89. Mihran's theoretical results from a square velocity distribution are also shown in Figure 88. It is seen that a better agreement with experiment was obtained tending to suggest that in this particular experimental set up, a half-Maxwellian distribution of velocities was obtained.

4.5 FINAL COMMENTS

Readers will doubtless feel that the current position of the subject is unsatisfactory. Despite this, however, one feels that a pattern is beginning to emerge.

It appears that, despite the limitations referred to by Carrol, the density function analysis method gives reasonable results because both Watkins and G. Gray obtained similar results and Bloom and Vural achieved reasonable success in accounting for some of Mihran's results; their analysis was also based on the density function method. Carrol's method gave results in agreement with this, although he used a different approach. The question of the velocity distribution one should use is still open to question. Watkins and Yadavalli used different velocity distributions and obtained similar results, the differences being slight, but Bloom and Vural obtained significant differences from the theoretical work of Mihran. The experimental work of Mihran, as explained by Bloom and Vural, tends to suggest that a half-Maxwellian distribution is the most suitable in that case. Far more experimental work will have to be carried out before the issue can be resolved.

It is a particularly difficult problem because each system will produce different distributions and an accurate method of measuring them is needed before one can proceed further experimentally. Beyond this point the situation is still very fluid; some analyses show that the multi-velocity beam does not drastically alter the results obtained in Chapters 2 and 3, probably because there is some measure of agreement on the fact that for small velocity spreads (small compared with the mean velocity) the mono-velocity theory applies. In practice the velocity spreads can be made small [Beck, 31]. The exception to this is noise. There has been some effort to apply these theories to noise on electron beams (Siegman *et al.* [109] for example) particularly in attempts to reduce it. This is a subject on its own which is not pursued here, but

Smullin and Haus [110] are two authorities on this subject and their book provides a starting point. Two workers have suggested, however, that multi-velocity beams do make significant changes in the theories of Chapters 2 and 3. Siegman [104] suggested that three waves propagate instead of two and Berghammer [106] suggested that the fast space-charge wave of the mono-velocity theory is replaced by a fast wave packet which decays with distance. This could account for the damping of the r.f. current with distance observed by Mihran (Figures 85 and 86). Thus, Berghammer provides a very different explanation of Mihran's experimental results. Unfortunately his work depends to a large extent on a plasma theory concept and we will not pursue it further. There have been no other comments on Berghammer's and Siegman's theories since their publication apart from Mihran's use of Siegman's analysis, but Caulton et al. [111] also observed similar evidence of damping.

Finally, it is obvious that there is still a long way to go before adequate information will be available to enable one to draw more definite conclusions. It would probably expedite matters if a more detailed investigation were carried out into the suggestions referred to above before new approaches were attempted, and it could be that Berghammer's approach will prove fruitful.

CHAPTER 5

Power Flow and Space-Charge Waves

The first known attempt to apply power-flow theories to space-charge waves was made by Chu in an unpublished memorandum. He derived an expression for what he called 'kinetic power' and subsequently showed that, in the slow space-charge wave the kinetic power is negative and in the fast space-charge wave the kinetic power is positive. Chu later referred to his work at a conference on electron devices, but so far as can be ascertained it was never published.

5.1 THE WORK OF PIERCE, WALKER AND THEIR CO-WORKERS

Pierce [15] and Walker [112] soon followed up Chu's work, and our study of power flow and space-charge waves is introduced by a discussion of the work of these two teams.

5.1.1. The work of Pierce

Pierce gave a general discussion which gives a most useful introduction to the subject.

One fundamental point which must be stressed is that since the group velocity of the wave is the velocity at which signal information is propagated, it is the group velocity that gives the direction in which the energy flows. The power flow is equal to the total stored energy per unit length W, times the group velocity. Therefore, if P is the power flow,

$$P = Wu_g$$

where u_g is the group velocity. It is seen in Section 2.2.5 that in the case of an infinite beam, the group velocity of both the fast and the slow space-charge wave is u_0. Therefore, in this particular case

$$P = Wu_0 . \qquad 5.1$$

Suppose that a beam is modulated by an a.c. voltage V and that this modulates the electron velocity but not the convection current density (i.e. the modulating gap is small). The total velocity is now $(u_0 + v)$ and the total accelerating voltage is $(V_0 + V)$

therefore $\qquad u_0 + v = \sqrt{[2\eta(V_0 + V)]}.$

Assuming V is small this gives

$$v = \frac{V\eta}{\sqrt{(2\eta V_0)}} = \frac{V\eta}{u_0}$$

therefore $\qquad V = \frac{u_0}{\eta} \cdot v \,.$

Introducing now a quantity U_V which is analogous to an a.c. voltage. U_V is defined by

$$U_V = -\frac{u_0 v}{\eta} = -V \qquad\qquad 5.2$$

and if we define an a.c. characteristic impedance Z, where

$$Z = U_V/J \,,$$

Eqn 2.30 gives

$$Z = \frac{u_0}{\eta\rho_0}(\pm\delta_1) = \frac{-u_0}{\varepsilon_0\omega_p^2}(\pm\delta_1)\,.$$

Therefore, if δ_1 is negative – the fast wave (Section 2.2.5), Z is positive, and if δ_1 is positive – the slow wave, Z is negative. Hence it is seen that for the slow wave the power flow is negative and, since u_0 is positive, the energy stored per unit length must also be negative, [from Eqn 5.1]. Similarly, the power flow and energy stored are positive for the fast wave.

Consider the system shown in Figure 90. An unmodulated beam flows through two modulating/de-modulating systems A and B. The electron velocity, the group velocity and the phase velocity are all in the positive z direction. Now it is arranged that a slow wave only is set up at A, and that the slow wave is entirely removed at B so that the beam beyond B is again un-modulated. It was shown above that on a slow wave, the power flow is negative; it is in the negative z direction. It follows, therefore, that to set up the slow wave at A power must be removed from the beam, and to remove the slow wave at B power must be put in, as shown in the diagram. The converse is true for the fast wave.

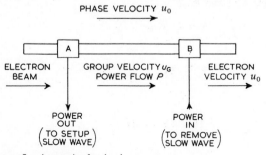

Note: Power flow is negative for the slow wave.

Figure 90. Illustration of the negative power flow of the slow space-charge wave

In Section 2.2.5 it was shown that for the slow wave, the charge density modulation and the velocity modulation are out of phase by π. Therefore, the charge density is greatest where the velocity is less than average and it is smallest where the velocity is greater than average, so that the electron beam has less kinetic energy in the presence of the slow wave than it does in the absence of the slow wave. If the observer moves with the slow wave, he sees the electrons moving in a constant electric field (constant in time) and thus, since the velocity of the electrons varies as the square root of the potential, the electrons move more slowly in regions of low potential and, therefore, they are bunched together in these regions. Since the total electron velocity is the sum of the wave velocity plus the electron velocity (relative to the wave velocity), the electrons are bunched in regions of least total electron velocity. The kinetic energy of the slow wave is thus negative. The converse is true for the fast wave, the kinetic energy being positive in that case.

Whilst this is a qualitative argument, it illustrates some important fundamental properties of space-charge waves. The characteristic impedance Z and the 'voltage' U_V which were introduced earlier are due to Chu. This work was soon followed by a paper by Louisell and Pierce [113], in which a far more rigorous analysis of power flow in beam devices was given.

From Eqns A1.1 and A1.2

$$\nabla \times \mathbf{E} = -\frac{\partial \mathbf{B}}{\partial t}$$

and

$$\nabla \times \mathbf{H} = \frac{\partial \mathbf{D}}{\partial t} + \mathbf{J}$$

we obtain

$$\mathbf{H} . \nabla \times \mathbf{E} = -\mathbf{H} \frac{\partial \mathbf{B}}{\partial t} \qquad 5.3$$

and

$$\mathbf{E} . \nabla \times \mathbf{H} = \mathbf{E} \frac{\partial \mathbf{D}}{\partial t} + \mathbf{E} . \mathbf{J}. \qquad 5.4$$

Combining Eqns 5.3 and 5.4 gives

$$\mathbf{H} . \nabla \times \mathbf{E} - \mathbf{E} . \nabla \times \mathbf{H} = -\mathbf{H} \frac{\partial \mathbf{B}}{\partial t} - \mathbf{E} \frac{\partial \mathbf{D}}{\partial t} - \mathbf{E} . \mathbf{J}$$

therefore

$$\nabla . (\mathbf{E} \times \mathbf{H}) + \mathbf{E} . \mathbf{J} = -\left[\mathbf{E} \frac{\partial \mathbf{D}}{\partial t} + \mathbf{H} \frac{\partial \mathbf{B}}{\partial t} \right]$$

therefore

$$\nabla . P_e + \mathbf{E} . \mathbf{J} = -\tfrac{1}{2} \frac{\partial}{\partial t} (\varepsilon \mathbf{E}^2 + \mu \mathbf{H}^2) \qquad 5.5$$

where $P_e = (\mathbf{E} \times \mathbf{H})$ the Poynting vector [114].

Consider now the case in which electrons are constrained to move only in the z direction: on linearizing we have:
the equation of motion

$$-\eta E_z = \frac{\partial v}{\partial t} + u_0 \frac{\partial v}{\partial z}$$

the equation for conservation of charge

$$\nabla . J_z = -\frac{\partial \rho}{\partial t} = \frac{\partial J_z}{\partial z}$$

and

$$J_z = \rho_0 v + \rho u_0 \,.$$

These give, omitting the suffix z,

$$E.J = -\frac{1}{\eta} \left[\frac{\partial v}{\partial t} + u_0 \frac{\partial v}{\partial z} \right] J \,. \qquad 5.6$$

Now define P_k as

$$-\frac{1}{2\eta} (J_0 + J)(u_0^2 + 2u_0 v)$$

and W_k as

$$-\frac{1}{2\eta} \left[-\rho_0(u_0^2 + 2u_0 v + v^2) + \rho(u_0^2 + 2u_0 v) \right] \,.$$

Using these definitions, Eqn 5.6 becomes

$$E.J = \frac{\partial W_k}{\partial t} + \frac{\partial P_k}{\partial t} \,. \qquad 5.7$$

Combining Eqns 5.5 and 5.7 and putting

$$\tfrac{1}{2}(\varepsilon \mathbf{E}^2 + \mu \mathbf{H}^2) = W_e$$

gives

$$\nabla.(P_e + P_k) + \frac{\partial}{\partial t}(W_e + W_k) = 0 \qquad 5.8$$

P_e is the Poynting vector which is the electro-magnetic energy flow per unit area. W_e is the electro-magnetic stored energy per unit volume associated with the total electric and magnetic fields. In a similar way, P_k can be defined as the kinetic power flow of the beam per unit area and W_k can be defined as the kinetic energy in the beam per unit volume. This kinetic power is that referred to by Chu. Note that P_k and W_k were chosen so that Eqn 5.8 holds for a linear system, although the expressions were not linear.

When dealing with complex a.c. quantities that vary as exp $(j\omega t)$, the average power flow per unit area in the z direction P_z is

$$P_z = \tfrac{1}{4}\left[(\mathbf{E} \times H^*) + (E^* \times \mathbf{H}) - \frac{mu_0}{e}(vJ^* + v^*J)\right] \qquad 5.9$$

where E^* is the complex conjugate of E and similarly for the other a.c. quantities.

In the case of space-charge waves which vary as $\exp\left[j(\omega t - \gamma z)\right]$ and in which the electric field is purely longitudinal, the electro-magnetic power flow is zero and the power flow is purely kinetic.

In practice, however, the electron beam is in a conducting cylinder and the electric field is not purely longitudinal, consequently there is an electro-magnetic power flow. Since $E_z = j\gamma V$, V being the potential, we define an electro-magnetic power flow P_{el} associated with the convection current J so that

$$P_{el} = \tfrac{1}{4}\left[VJ^* + V^*J\right].$$

Combining $E_z = j\gamma V$ with Eqn 5.6, P_{el} becomes

$$P_{el} = -\tfrac{1}{4}\,\frac{m}{e}\,u_0\left[\frac{(\omega - \gamma u_0)}{\gamma u_0}\right]\left[vJ^* + v^*J\right] \qquad 5.10$$

and the ratio $\quad \dfrac{P_{el}}{P_k} = \dfrac{(\omega - \gamma u_0)}{\gamma u_0}.$ \hfill 5.11

But from Eqn 2.26, $(\omega - \gamma u_0) = \pm\omega_q$ (substituting ω_q for ω_p to take account of the proximity of the conducting cylinder). Therefore Eqn 5.11 becomes

$$P_{el}/P_k = \pm\omega_q/\omega$$

assuming that $\omega_q \ll \omega$ which is a reasonable assumption for space-charge waves in practical devices.

Thus, the electro-magnetic power flow lies between zero (when the electric field is purely longitudinal) and P_{el} (when the transverse electric field is much greater than the longitudinal electric field). It should be stressed that when $\omega_q \ll \omega$ the electro-magnetic power of the space-charge wave is much less than the kinetic power.

5.1.2. The work of Walker

Walker's first paper [112] was not specifically concerned with space-charge waves, but he considered the problem of finding the a.c. energy and a.c. power flow in an electron beam when it interacts with an electromagnetic travelling-wave.

Nevertheless, some important issues are raised and we discuss the work briefly.

Normally in space-charge-wave theory, one assumes that the a.c. parts of the variables are small compared to the d.c. parts so that the equations of motion, continuity, etc. can be linearized by neglecting products of a.c. quantities. The question to be considered is, if the a.c. kinetic energy and the a.c. power flow are second order quantities in terms of the applied field, can the simple linearized analysis give us an answer to the problem?

As before we have

$$\rho = \frac{j\gamma\rho_0\eta E}{(\omega - \gamma u_0)^2} \qquad \text{(From Eqn 2.12)}$$

and since

$$J = \rho_0 v + \rho u_0 \quad (=\omega_p/\gamma)$$

$$J = \frac{j\omega\rho_0\eta E}{(\omega - \gamma u_0)^2}.$$

In the case of a sheet beam, if E does not vary in the x direction, and the beam thickness is d in the y direction, the tangential magnetic fields at the point $(+y)$ and $(-y)$ are given by

$$H_{x(-y)} - H_{x(+y)} = \frac{j\omega\rho_0\eta E}{(\omega - \gamma u_0)^2}\, d.$$

The power entering the beam per unit area is then

$$= \tfrac{1}{2}R\big[E^*(H_{x(-y)} - H_{x(+y)})\big]$$

$$= \tfrac{1}{2}R\left[\frac{j\omega\rho_0 d\eta}{(\omega - \gamma u_0)^2}\right]|E^2|.$$

Putting
$$\frac{\omega\rho_0 \, d\eta}{(\omega - \gamma u_0)^2} = F(\omega, \gamma)$$

the power absorbed in the beam per unit area

$$= \tfrac{1}{2} R[jF(\omega, \gamma)] |E^2| . \qquad 5.12$$

However, it is pointed out that the question asked was incomplete because the applied electric field is infinite in both space and time and no connection with the original state of the beam is established. This connection has to be established somehow. Assume the force on the electrons due to the field is equal to

$$-\xi a(z, t) \cos(\omega t - \gamma z)$$

where $a(z, t)$ is a function of both z and t,

  $a(z, t) \to 0$ as z (or t) $\to -\infty$, and

  $a(z, t) \to 1$ as z (or t) $\to$ (something large).

Assume also that $\partial a / \partial t$ and $\partial a / \partial z$ are small. Hence the field increases with z and t from zero to ξ as z (or t) becomes large. Suppose now that the number of electrons in the modulated beam, in the element between z and $(z + dz)$, with velocities between v and $(v + dv)$, is written as $f(z, t, v) \, dz \, dv$ so that the charge density at z and t is

$$\rho_0 \int_0^\infty f(z, v, t) \, dz \, dv$$

and f satisfies the equation

$$\frac{\partial f}{\partial t} + v \frac{\partial f}{\partial z} = \frac{\partial f}{\partial v} \, \xi a(z, t) \cos(\omega t - \gamma z) . \qquad 5.13$$

If we assume $f = f_0(v_0) + \xi f_1(z, v, t) + \xi^2 f_2(z, v, t)$, substituting into Eqn 5.13 and equating terms of the same order of ξ gives

$$\frac{\partial f_1}{\partial t} + v \frac{\partial f_1}{\partial z} = \frac{\partial f_0}{\partial v} \, a(z, t) \cos(\omega t - \gamma z) \qquad 5.14$$

and an identical equation in f_2.

Putting

$$f_1 = A_1 \cos(\omega t - \gamma z) + B_1 \sin(\omega t - \gamma z)$$

and

$$f_2 = C_1 + D_1 \cos(\omega t - \gamma z) + E_1 \sin(\omega t - \gamma z)$$

(where A_1, B_1, C_1, D_1 and E_1 are functions of z, t and v) and substituting into equations 5.14, values of A_1, B_1, C_1, D_1 and E_1 can be obtained. The details of the algebra are given in Walker's paper.

He showed that the expression for C_1 depends explicitly on the function $a(z, t)$ indicating that the problem depends on the way the field is formed. Hence the a.c. stored energy and the a.c. power flow are not uniquely determined by the first order state of the beam. The a.c. stored energy is proportional to

$$\frac{1}{2} \int_0^\infty f_2 v^2 \, dv$$

and the a.c. power flow is proportional to

$$\frac{1}{2} \int_0^\infty f_2 v^3 \, dv.$$

He considered special cases, the first in which $a(z, t)$ has no variation in z and the second in which $a(z, t)$ has no variation in t.

The detailed expressions obtained indicate that the stored energy could be negative as could the power flow. Negative energy stored implies that work was extracted from the original unmodulated beam when it was modulated. A beam with negative stored energy could be unstable because it could do work on its surroundings, thus increasing its modulation. It is shown that if the wave phase velocity is less than the velocity of the electrons in the beam, the stored energy is negative. Conversely, if the wave phase velocity is greater than the velocity of the electrons in the beam, the stored energy is positive.

To return to the point raised about the linear theory (p. 175), Walker showed that the results obtained from the more detailed analysis, for both the a.c. stored energy and the a.c. power flow, agreed with the results obtained from the linear analysis. A far more detailed investigation of these two approaches was later published by Walker [115]. He shows here that it is possible to find expressions for the second order quantities obtained in the expressions for a.c. stored energy and a.c. power flow, in terms of first order terms. It appears, therefore, that the simple linearized analysis can give a solution to the problem.

5.1.3. Discussion

The two approaches to the question given above are quite different. Essentially, the Louisell and Pierce approach is to find quadratic expressions in the first order quantities, that have the dimensions of power flow or of stored kinetic energy and which satisfy the conditions required, such as the various laws of conservation. Walker actually deals with non-linear equations (for small-signals), but these become cumbersome and consequently he looks for expressions for the second order quantities in terms of first order terms. He is then obliged to confirm that these two methods are equivalent.

As is so often the case, the Pierce approach is the simplest, but the possible objections raised by Walker obviously had to be investigated. It now appears that these objections can be circumvented. Both Pierce and Walker, who collaborated throughout this period, are agreed that this is so.

Having established the fundamental principles of this theory, it is of interest to give an example of the use to which it can be put. (In Section 3.3.4 a brief account was given of the double-stream interaction in terms of an interchange of energy between a fast and a slow space-charge wave.) Consider the resistive-wall amplifier in which the input device produces both the fast and the slow space-charge waves. Assuming they are produced with equal magnitudes, both waves induce charge in the resistive wall and thus dissipate power in the wall in equal amounts. The slow wave has negative power and its power becomes more negative as the beam gives up more and more power to the wall. Thus the slow space-charge wave increases (in space) exponentially. The fast space-charge wave has positive power and its power becomes less positive. Consequently its amplitude decreases exponentially as the beam traverses the resistive wall. If the output device is a long way from the input device the fast wave amplitude is negligible there.

It is now clear why attempts to reduce noise in a travelling-wave tube by passing the beam near a lossy circuit (Section 3.2.6) were unsuccessful. Only fast wave noise could be removed, but slow wave noise would be amplified. It is also clear that it was Chu's investigations into kinetic power that led him to suggest that passing a beam near a lossy circuit would produce amplification.

This introduction has already illustrated the usefulness of the concept of the energy of space-charge waves. One can visualize a multitude of applications and the vast amount of work this could lead to. Let us now look at the more recent work that has evolved from the work of the pioneers.

5.2 THE LATEST DEVELOPMENTS

There is not a vast amount of literature on this subject and, unfortunately, most of the work that has been published is devoted to electron beams as opposed to waves on electron beams.

Haus and Bobrof [116] considered the thin filamentary beam and produced an expression for the electro-magnetic power delivered by the beam into an a.c. field between two planes. They found that the essential sources of power from an electron beam are:

(a) Longitudinal kinetic power – from first order axial deceleration and acceleration of electrons.
(b) Transverse kinetic power – from second order axial deceleration and acceleration of electrons (due to transverse displacement of the beam).
(c) Potential power – from a displacement in a transverse d.c. electric field.

In 1962, Bobrof, Haus and Kluver [117] reviewed their small-signal power theorem referred to above as a result of E. L. Chu's [118] criticism of it. They re-derived the theorem in a simpler way. Whilst the bulk of this paper was concerned with the electron beam, these authors briefly discussed zero order waves on a Brillouin beam in free space.

They showed that the average power flow of a wave on such a beam was given by

$$P_{av} = u_{0(z)} \pi \varepsilon_0 \left(\frac{\omega}{\omega_p} \right) |V_0|^2 [F_1 + F_2] \qquad 5.15$$

where V_0 is the potential at the edge of the beam and where

$$F_1 = \frac{(\gamma b)}{2 I_1(\gamma b) K_0(\gamma b)} \frac{\{1 - [K_1(\gamma b) I_1(\gamma b)/K_0(\gamma b) I_0(\gamma b)]\}}{\left\{ \left(\frac{\omega}{\omega_p} \right) \pm [(\gamma b) I_1(\gamma b) K_0(\gamma b)]^{\frac{1}{2}} \right\}} \qquad 5.16$$

$$F_2 = \pm [I_0(\gamma b) K_0(\gamma b) \{(\gamma b) I_1(\gamma b) K_0(\gamma b)\}^{\frac{1}{2}}]^{-1}. \qquad 5.17$$

In both F_1 and F_2 the upper sign refers to the fast wave and the lower sign to the slow wave.

The energy stored per unit length W_{av} was found to be

$$W_{av} = \pi \varepsilon_0 \left(\frac{\omega}{\omega_p} \right) |V_0|^2 F_2 \qquad 5.18$$

F_2 is derived from purely kinetic variables, but F_1 includes both electro-magnetic and kinetic variables. Neglecting the electro-magnetic terms (as in Section 5.1.1) Eqns 5.15 and 5.18 give

$$P_{av}/W_{av} = u_{0(z)} = u_g \qquad \text{(as in Section 5.1.1)}$$

The functions F_1 and F_2 are plotted in Figures 91 and 92 for values of $(\omega/\omega_p) = 5$ and 10 for both the slow and fast waves. F_1 is always positive and small compared with F_2. F_2 is positive for fast waves, but negative for slow waves. It is seen that F_1 is different for slow and fast waves, the difference decreasing as (ω/ω_p) increases.

The ratio of electro-magnetic and kinetic power flow to pure kinetic power flow F_1/F_2, is shown in Figure 93. It is seen that F_1/F_2 has a maximum where γb is approximately 0·6. The electro-magnetic/kinetic power flow becomes more important the more the phase velocity of the wave differs from the beam velocity.

In the same journal Kluver [119] transformed the Haus-Bobrof small-signal power theorem into a form that lends itself to practical applications. He introduced the scalar and vector potentials. Once again, this paper was mainly concerned with the electron beam, but he

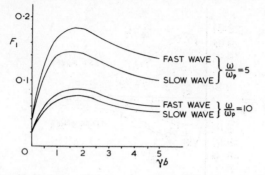

Figure 91. Variation of electro-magnetic and kinetic power flow

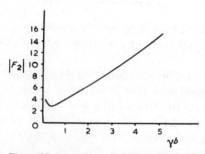

Figure 92. Variation of kinetic power flow

briefly considered slow waves on an excited beam. An expression for P_k/P_{el} was found:

$$\frac{P_k}{P_{el}} = \frac{\gamma u_0}{(\omega - \gamma u_0)} \left[1 - \frac{k^2}{\gamma^2} \right] \left[1 - \frac{I_1^2(\gamma b)}{I_0^2(\gamma b)} \right].$$

If $k^2 \ll \gamma^2$ and $I_0^2(\gamma b) \gg I_1^2(\gamma b)$ (i.e., if we have only slow waves and also a thin beam),

$$P_k/P_{el} = \gamma u_0/(\omega - \gamma u_0)$$

which is the expression Louisell and Pierce [113] derived [Eqn 5.11].

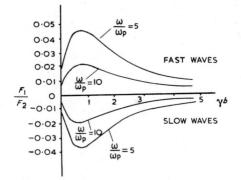

Figure 93. Variation of the ratio of electro-magnetic and kinetic power flow to pure kinetic power flow

Only two papers have been devoted exclusively to power flow in electron beam waves and both were concerned solely with the negative energy concept.

Beam [120], in a short letter, discussed the power flow in any electron beam wave, whether it be axial or transverse. He showed that the condition for the wave to carry negative power is that $u_0/u_p > 1$ where u_0 is the beam velocity and u_p is the phase velocity of the wave concerned. This means that $u_p < u_0$ which is the definition of the slow space-charge wave. One should bear in mind that this condition also applies to cyclotron waves.

Sturrock [121] asked the question 'in what sense do slow waves carry negative energy?'. Consider a complicated modulating device that extracts r.f. energy from the beam, thus setting up only the slow wave, and which then converts the r.f. energy extracted into d.c. energy which is used to accelerate the beam. In that case, zero physical energy has been given to, or removed from, the system. Consequently, one cannot say that physical energy of the slow wave is negative, but only that the energy of a slow wave, excited in a particular way, is negative. Thus one must ask the question Sturrock posed and an appropriate generalization of the small-signal power theorem must be sought. He showed that it is possible to set up a small-signal energy theorem for any dynamical system. The Lagrangian function [Goldstein, 95] describing such a system, is shown to be a quadratic function and this yields linearized equations for the system in terms of a stress tensor. It is this generalization of the small-signal power theorem, which is applicable to any dynamical system, that enables one to assert that all slow waves carry negative energy.

Whilst Sturrock's question is valid, and it is interesting to note that no other comments have been made, one might ask, when considering his example of a complicated modulating device and beam system quoted above, what happens when the beam is accelerated? Does not this alter the kinetic power of the beam (an increasing wave is set up now) so that a physical negative energy may be possible?

5.3 FINAL COMMENTS

There is little to add to the discussion of Section 5.1.3. It is now clear that the theories of the pioneers have, in general, been substantiated. The recent work, whilst extending these theories a little, has not in any way altered the basic concepts of L. J. Chu. The lack of controversy, alternative suggestions and literature is very marked indeed, particularly for such an important topic.

Some possible applications of the power flow theories have already been indicated, but the most useful application may well be in attempting to explain noise on electron devices. Haus and Robinson [122] is a typical example of such an attempt, but this is a vast subject and is not pursued further.

CHAPTER 6

General Conclusions

It is clear that two, unattenuated, longitudinal space-charge waves propagate on an extended electron beam confined by an infinite or very high longitudinal magnetic focusing field, provided the beam is moving and provided also that it is assumed that all electrons in the beam have the same d.c. velocity.

The two waves are dispersive waves and have the same group velocity, but their phase velocities are different. One has a phase velocity slightly less than the electron beam velocity, and the other has a phase velocity slightly greater than the electron beam velocity. Thus, the two waves are called the slow and the fast space-charge wave respectively. Because both waves have a phase velocity very close to the velocity of the electron beam, and this velocity is usually much less than the velocity of light, space-charge waves are often called slow waves.

If the beam is confined in a coaxial conducting drift-tube, the natural frequency of plasma oscillations is reduced and the waves disperse less. When the beam completely fills the drift-tube, the waves are non-dispersive.

A r.f. disturbance will propagate along the beam by means of these two space-charge waves, which form an interference pattern. Each electron in the beam is set vibrating separately at an angular frequency ω_p, about its equilibrium position (it can oscillate only at an angular frequency ω_p). The phases and amplitudes of the oscillations are different, however, and such as to produce the effect of a wave as viewed by a stationary observer. The wave propagates at the same angular frequency as the disturbance and this is, therefore, a Doppler shifted frequency of the angular frequency ω_p of the moving electrons.

If the longitudinal magnetic field strength is reduced to such an extent that $B_c < (4\omega_p)/\eta$ an additional pair of space-charge waves propagates. These are associated with the cyclotron frequency ω_c and have a plasma frequency 'reduction' factor which is greater than unity.

Both the power flow and stored energy of the fast and slow space-charge waves are positive and negative respectively.

It has been shown, theoretically, that there are a variety of mechanisms (other than interaction with propagating structures) by which increasing space-charge waves can be made to propagate on a single electron beam. In general, one applies a periodic change in electric field to the beam or arranges for the beam to interact with the charge induced, by the beam, on to the wall of the drift-tube. The admittance of the wall has to be resistive or inductive.

Increasing space-charge waves also propagate on a system containing two beams, provided that the beams are in close proximity to each other and the current densities of each beam are high enough.

If the beams are confined by an infinite longitudinal magnetic focusing field, each has a fast and slow space-charge wave propagating on it (assuming they are excited). Coupling between the slow wave on the fast beam and the fast wave on the slow beam may take place to produce an increasing wave. Briefly, the mechanism is as follows. The slow wave loses energy to the fast wave and, since its energy becomes more negative, it increases in space. Similarly, the fast wave decreases. The fast wave on the fast beam and the slow wave on the slow beam remain unattenuated. The condition for coupling to take place and for the increasing wave to propagate is

$$\omega_p 2\sqrt{2} > \{2\omega - \gamma(u_{01} + u_{02})\} \ .$$

If the strength of the longitudinal magnetic focusing field is reduced, cyclotron waves propagate on each beam in addition to the space-charge waves. It is now possible for coupling between cyclotron waves and between cyclotron and space-charge waves to take place. This is in addition to coupling between space-charge waves as before.

Direct experimental verification of the suggested methods of producing increasing space-charge waves, on both single and double electron beams, has been obtained, but none of the amplifiers had a significantly better performance than the travelling-wave tube. It appears that the difficulties involved in coupling the signal to the beam, of exciting the space-charge waves and of removing the output are considerable. Also, if one has to use a helix at all, and this is often used to couple signals onto beams, why not extend it the whole length of the tube and construct a travelling-wave tube? In the double-stream amplifier one has the added difficulty of keeping the two beams in synchronism.

Direct experimental verification of the theories of propagation of un-attenuated space-charge waves has not been obtained, indeed few experiments designed to do this have been performed. Support for these theories has been obtained merely as a by-product of experimental work on devices, particularly the klystron, and on electron beam optics. Nevertheless, there is little suggestion that the final conclusions are incorrect although the development of the theory was not without controversy.

The effect, on the mono-velocity space-charge-wave theory, of introducing the fact that in practice the beam has a velocity distribution, is not at all clear.

Some workers have suggested that the multi-velocity beam makes little difference, and this is probably true if the velocity distribution is small. Other workers have suggested that there are significant changes in the mono-velocity theory; this is probably true if the velocity distribution is not small. One suggestion is that the fast wave is replaced by a fast wave packet and this theory gives results that agreed quite well with some experimental results. Another suggestion is that in addition to the fast and the slow space-charge waves, a fast wave in the opposite direction propagates, although this is not supported by the experimental evidence. However, the experimental evidence is very limited and the conclusions on the multi-velocity theory must be regarded as purely tentative.

APPENDIX 1

Maxwell's Equations

The basic equations that describe all macroscopic electromagnetic phenomena are:

$$\nabla \times \mathbf{E} = -\frac{\partial \mathbf{B}}{\partial t} \qquad \text{A1.1}$$

$$\nabla \times \mathbf{H} = \frac{\partial \mathbf{D}}{\partial t} + \mathbf{J} \qquad \text{A1.2}$$

The components of these equations, in cylindrical-polar co-ordinates, are

$$\frac{1}{r}\frac{\partial E_z}{\partial \theta} - \frac{\partial E_\theta}{\partial z} = -\frac{\partial B_r}{\partial t} \qquad \text{A1.3}$$

$$\frac{\partial E_r}{\partial z} - \frac{\partial E_z}{\partial r} = -\frac{\partial B_\theta}{\partial t} \qquad \text{A1.4}$$

$$\frac{1}{r}\frac{\partial}{\partial r}(rE_\theta) - \frac{1}{r}\frac{\partial E_r}{\partial \theta} = -\frac{\partial B_z}{\partial t} \qquad \text{A1.5}$$

$$\frac{1}{r}\frac{\partial H_z}{\partial \theta} - \frac{\partial H_\theta}{\partial z} = \frac{\partial D_r}{\partial t} + J_r \qquad \text{A1.6}$$

$$\frac{\partial H_r}{\partial z} - \frac{\partial H_z}{\partial r} = \frac{\partial D_\theta}{\partial t} + J_\theta \qquad \text{A1.7}$$

$$\frac{1}{r}\frac{\partial}{\partial r}(rH_\theta) - \frac{1}{r}\frac{\partial H_r}{\partial \theta} = \frac{\partial D_z}{\partial t} + J_z \qquad \text{A1.8}$$

(using $\mathbf{B} = \mu_0 \mathbf{H}$ and $\mathbf{D} = \varepsilon_0 \mathbf{E}$).

A1.1, A1.2 and the continuity equation on manipulation give

$$\nabla \cdot \mathbf{B} = 0 \qquad \text{A1.9}$$
$$\nabla \cdot \mathbf{D} = \rho . \qquad \text{A1.10}$$

The use of Maxwell's equations implies that

   (a) An electron is a point charge in motion and

   (b) An assembly of electrons is a continuum.

The Electronic Theory of Space-Charge Waves

(Based on Hutter's *Beam and Wave Electronics in Microwave Tubes*, copyright 1960, D. van Nostrand Company Inc., Princeton, N.J.)

The equations required are A1.1, A1.2, A1.10, Lorentz and continuity. We consider the rectilinear flow case (Section 2.2). Therefore, the total current density can have only a z component given by

$$(\nabla \times \mathbf{H})_z = \left(\mathbf{J} + \frac{\partial \mathbf{D}}{\partial t}\right)_z.$$

But

$$(\nabla \times \mathbf{H})_z = \frac{\partial H_y}{\partial x} - \frac{\partial H_y}{\partial y} = 0,$$

therefore

$$J_T = 0.$$

Since div (curl) of any vector is zero

$$\frac{\partial}{\partial z}\left[J_z + \varepsilon_0 \frac{\partial E_z}{\partial t}\right] = 0,$$

and

$$J_T - J_z = \varepsilon_0 \frac{\partial E_z}{\partial t}. \qquad \text{A2.1}$$

The continuity equation gives

$$\nabla . J_z + \frac{\partial \rho}{\partial t} = 0,$$

therefore

$$\frac{\partial J_z}{\partial z} + j\omega\rho = 0. \qquad \text{A2.2}$$

Eqn A1.10 gives

$$\varepsilon_0 \frac{\partial E_z}{\partial z} = \rho,$$

189

and the Lorentz equation gives

$$\mathrm{d}v_z/dt = -\eta E_z$$

neglecting magnetic forces. Now

$$J_0 + J_z = (\rho_0 + \rho)(u_0 + v_z)$$

and therefore

$$J_0 = \rho_0 u_0 , \qquad\qquad\qquad \text{A2.3}$$

$$J_z = u_0 \rho + \rho_0 v_z \quad \text{(ignoring 2nd order terms)}.$$

therefore

$$v_z = \frac{1}{\rho_0}(J_z - u_0 \rho). \qquad\qquad\qquad \text{A2.4}$$

But

$$\rho = -\frac{1}{j\omega}\frac{\partial J_z}{\partial z}, \qquad\qquad\qquad \text{A2.5}$$

therefore

$$v_z = \frac{u_0}{J_0}\left(J_z + \frac{u_0}{j\omega}\cdot\frac{\partial J_z}{\partial z}\right). \qquad\qquad\qquad \text{A2.6}$$

The Lorentz equation gives

$$\frac{d\mathbf{u}}{dt} = \frac{\partial \mathbf{u}}{\partial t} + \frac{\partial \mathbf{u}}{\partial z}\cdot\frac{\partial z}{\partial t} = -\eta(E_0 + E_z) ,$$

therefore

$$\frac{du_0}{dt} = -\eta E_0 ,$$

and

$$j\omega v_z + \frac{\partial}{\partial z}(u_0 + v_z).(u_0 + v_z) = -\eta E_z ,$$

therefore

$$\left(j\omega + \frac{\partial u_0}{\partial z}\right)v_z + u_0 \frac{\partial v_z}{\partial z} = -\eta E_z . \qquad\qquad \text{A2.7}$$

Now put

$$J_z = \frac{X}{u_0}e^{-j\omega\tau_0} \qquad\qquad\qquad \text{A2.8}$$

where τ_0 is the d.c. transit time.
Therefore

$$\tau_0 = t - t_0 = \int_0^z \frac{dz}{u_0} .$$

Therefore Eqn A2.6 becomes

$$v_z = \frac{u_0}{J_0}\left[\frac{X}{u_0}e^{-j\omega\tau_0} + \frac{u_0}{j\omega}\frac{\partial}{\partial\tau_0}\left(\frac{X}{u_0}e^{-j\omega\tau_0} \right)\frac{\partial\tau_0}{\partial z} \right].$$

Therefore

$$v_z = \frac{u_0}{J_0}\left[\frac{X}{u_0}e^{-j\omega\tau_0} + \frac{u_0}{j\omega}\left\{ e^{-j\omega\tau_0}\left(u_0\frac{\partial X}{\partial\tau_0} - \frac{\partial u_0}{\partial\tau_0}X \right)\frac{1}{u_0^2} \right.\right.$$
$$\left.\left. - j\omega e^{-j\omega\tau_0}\cdot\frac{X}{u_0} \right\}\frac{1}{u_0} \right].$$

This becomes

$$v_z = \frac{e^{-j\omega\tau_0}}{j\omega J_0}\left[\frac{\partial X}{\partial\tau_0} - \frac{\partial u_0}{\partial\tau}\cdot\frac{X}{u_0} \right]. \qquad \text{A2.9}$$

Substituting for v_z in Eqn A2.7 we get, on manipulation,

$$\frac{\partial^2 X}{\partial\tau_0^2} - \frac{X}{u_0}\frac{\partial u_0^2}{\partial\tau_0^2} = -\eta j\omega J_z e^{j\omega\tau_0}E_z. \qquad \text{A2.10}$$

Eqns A2.7 and A2.6 combined give, on manipulation

$$\frac{\partial^2 J_z}{\partial z^2} + \frac{\partial J_z}{\partial z}\left(\frac{3}{u_0}\frac{\partial u_0}{\partial z} + \frac{2j\omega}{u_0} \right)$$
$$+ J_z\left(\frac{2j\omega}{u_0^2}\frac{\partial u_0}{\partial z} - \frac{\omega^2}{u_0^2} \right) = -\eta j\frac{\omega J_0}{u_0^3}E_z. \qquad \text{A2.11}$$

Now we are concerned with the case when u_0 is constant. Since $J_T = 0$ Eqn A2.1 gives

$$J_z = -j\omega\varepsilon_0 E_z = \frac{X}{u_0}e^{-j\omega\tau_0} \qquad \text{[from A2.8]}$$

and therefore, Eqn A2.10 becomes

$$\frac{\partial^2 X}{\partial\tau_0^2} - \left(\frac{X}{u_0}\frac{J_0\eta}{\varepsilon_0} \right) = 0 ,$$

therefore
$$\frac{\partial^2 X}{\partial \tau_0^2} + \omega_p^2 X = 0 \qquad\qquad \text{A2.12}$$

therefore
$$X = A' e^{j\omega_p\tau_0} + B' e^{-j\omega_p\tau_0}.$$

But since $J_z = \dfrac{X}{u_0} e^{-j\omega\tau_0}$ and $z = u_0\tau_0$,

$$J_z = \frac{1}{u_0} \cdot \left[A' e^{-j(\omega-\omega_p)\frac{z}{u_0}} + B' e^{-j(\omega+\omega_p)\frac{z}{u_0}} \right]$$

Thus, J_z has two wave functions with propagation constant

$$\gamma_{1,2} = \frac{\omega}{u_0} \pm \frac{\omega_p}{u_0}.$$

Similarly, by putting $J_T \neq 0$, it is possible to find the values of γ for the finite beam case.

Derivation of the Equations used for the Analyses of a Beam in a Finite Longitudinal Magnetic Field

Assuming a.c. quantities vary as $\exp\left[j(\omega t - \gamma z)\right]$, and that we have an axially symmetric field, Eqns A1.4, A1.6 and A1.8 become (omitting suffix t):

$$-j\gamma E_r - \frac{\partial E_z}{\partial r} = -j\omega B_\theta .\qquad \text{A3.1}$$

$$\frac{1}{r}\frac{\partial H_z}{\partial \theta} + j\gamma H_\theta = j\omega\varepsilon_0 E_r + J_r .\qquad \text{A3.2}$$

$$\frac{1}{r}\frac{\partial}{\partial r}(rH_\theta) - \frac{1}{r}\frac{\partial H_r}{\partial \theta} = j\omega\varepsilon_0 E_z + J_z .\qquad \text{A3.3}$$

Therefore Eqns A3.2 and A3.3 become

$$H_\theta = \frac{j\omega\varepsilon_0 E_r}{j\gamma} + \frac{J_r}{j\gamma}\qquad \text{A3.4}$$

and

$$\frac{1}{r}\frac{\partial}{\partial r}(rH_\theta) = j\omega\varepsilon_0 E_z + J_z .\qquad \text{A3.5}$$

Eqn A3.4 gives

$$H_\theta = \frac{\omega\varepsilon_0}{\gamma} E_r - \frac{j}{\gamma}\cdot J_r .\qquad \text{A3.6}$$

Eqn A3.1 gives

$$-j\gamma E_r = \frac{\partial E_z}{\partial r} - j\omega\mu_0 H_\theta ,$$

therefore

$$-j\gamma E_r = \frac{\partial E_z}{\partial r} - j\omega\mu_0\left[\frac{\omega\varepsilon_0}{\gamma} E_r - \frac{j}{\gamma} J_r\right]\qquad \text{(from A3.6)}$$

therefore
$$-\frac{j}{\gamma}[\gamma^2 - k^2]E_r = \frac{\partial E_z}{\partial r} - \frac{\omega u_0}{\gamma} J_r$$

(where $k^2 = \omega^2/c^2$).
But for space-charge waves $\gamma^2 \gg k^2$

therefore
$$\gamma^2 E_r = -\frac{\gamma}{j}\frac{\partial E_z}{\partial r} + \frac{\omega\mu_0}{j} J_r,$$

therefore
$$E_r = \frac{j}{\gamma}\frac{\partial E_z}{\partial r} - \frac{j\omega\mu_0}{\gamma^2}\cdot J_r. \qquad \text{A3.7}_1$$

Now $J_r \simeq \omega\varepsilon_0 E_z$

therefore
$$\frac{j\omega\mu_0 J_r}{\gamma^2} = j\frac{k^2}{\gamma^2} E_z.$$

Therefore Eqn A3.7$_1$ becomes
$$E_r = \frac{j}{\gamma}\cdot\frac{\partial E_z}{\partial r} - j\frac{k^2}{\gamma^2} E_z,$$

therefore
$$E_r \simeq \frac{j}{\gamma}\frac{\partial E_z}{\partial r}. \qquad \text{A3.7}_2$$

Eqn A3.5 becomes, therefore,
$$\frac{1}{r}\frac{\partial}{\partial r}\left\{r\left[\frac{\omega\varepsilon_0}{\gamma}E_r - \frac{j}{\gamma}J_r\right]\right\} = j\omega\varepsilon_0 E_z + J_z, \qquad \text{(from A3.6)}$$

$$\therefore \frac{1}{r}\left[\frac{\omega\varepsilon_0}{\gamma}\cdot\frac{j}{\gamma}\right]\frac{\partial}{\partial r}\left(r\frac{\partial E_z}{\partial r}\right) - j\omega\varepsilon_0 E_z = \frac{1}{r}\frac{j}{\gamma}\frac{\partial}{\partial r}(rJ_r) + J_z \qquad \text{(using A3.7}_2\text{)}$$

$$\therefore \frac{1}{r}\frac{\partial}{\partial r}\left(r\frac{\partial E_z}{\partial r}\right) - \gamma^2 E_z = \frac{\gamma^2}{j\omega\varepsilon_0}J_z + \frac{\gamma}{\omega\varepsilon_0}\frac{1}{r}\frac{\partial}{\partial r}(rJ_r) \qquad \text{A3.8}_1$$

or
$$\nabla^2 E_z = \frac{\gamma^2}{j\omega\varepsilon_0}J_z + \frac{\gamma}{\omega\varepsilon_0}\frac{1}{r}\frac{\partial}{\partial r}(rJ_r). \qquad \text{A3.8}_2$$

Eqn A1.3 becomes
$$j\gamma E_\theta = -j\omega\mu_0 H_r,$$

therefore
$$H_r = -\frac{\gamma}{\omega\mu_0} . E_\theta .$$ A3.10

Eqn A1.5 becomes
$$\frac{1}{r}\frac{\partial}{\partial r}(rE_\theta) = -j\omega\mu_0 H_z .$$ A3.11

Eqn A1.7 becomes
$$-j\gamma H_r - \frac{\partial H_z}{\partial r} = j\omega\varepsilon_0 E_\theta + J_\theta ,$$ A1.7a

therefore
$$jE_\theta\left(\frac{\gamma^2}{\omega\mu_0} - \omega\varepsilon_0\right) = \frac{\partial H_z}{\partial r} + J_\theta .$$ (using A3.10)

Since $\gamma^2 \gg k^2$

$$j\frac{\gamma^2}{\omega\mu_0} . E_\theta = \frac{\partial H_z}{\partial r} + J_\theta ,$$

$$\therefore \frac{j\gamma^2}{\omega\mu_0} . \frac{1}{r}\frac{\partial}{\partial r}(rE_\theta) = \frac{1}{r}\frac{\partial}{\partial r}\left(r\frac{\partial H_z}{\partial r}\right) + \frac{1}{r}\frac{\partial}{\partial r}(rJ_\theta)$$

$$\therefore \frac{-j\gamma^2}{\omega\mu_0} . j\omega\mu_0 H_z = \frac{1}{r}\frac{\partial}{\partial r}\left(r\frac{\partial H_z}{\partial r}\right) + \frac{1}{r}\frac{\partial}{\partial r}(rJ_\theta)$$ (using A3.11)

$$\therefore \frac{1}{r}\frac{\partial}{\partial r}\left(r\frac{\partial H_z}{\partial r}\right) - \gamma^2 H_z = -\frac{1}{r}\frac{\partial}{\partial r}(rJ_\theta) .$$ A3.12

Eqn A3.10, on re-writing, becomes

$$E_\theta = -\frac{\omega\mu_0}{\gamma} . H_r .$$ A3.13

Eqn A1.7a, combined with A3.13, gives

$$-j\gamma H_r + j\omega\varepsilon_0\frac{\omega\mu_0}{\gamma} H_r = \frac{\partial H_z}{\partial r} + J_\theta$$

therefore since $\gamma^2 \gg k^2$

$$H_r = j\gamma\left[\frac{\partial H_z}{\partial r} + J_\theta\right].$$ A3.14

Eqns A3.1 and A3.3 combined with A1.9, give

$$\frac{1}{\omega\mu_0} \cdot \frac{1}{r} \frac{\partial}{\partial r} \left[r \left(\gamma E_r - j \frac{\partial E_z}{\partial r} \right) \right] = J_z + j\omega\varepsilon_0 E_z \, ,$$

and simple manipulation gives

$$\frac{1}{r} \frac{\partial}{\partial r} \left(r \frac{\partial E_z}{\partial r} \right) - (\gamma^2 - k^2) E_z = j\omega\mu_0 J_z - j\gamma \frac{\rho}{\varepsilon_0} \, . \qquad \text{A3.15}$$

Also the continuity equation becomes

$$\nabla \cdot [(\rho_0 + \rho)(\bar{u}_0 + \bar{v})] = -\partial\rho/\partial t$$

therefore

$$\nabla \cdot [\rho\bar{u}_0 + \rho_0\bar{v}] = -j\omega\rho$$

therefore

$$u_0(-j\gamma\rho) + \rho_0 \nabla \cdot \bar{v} = -j\omega\rho$$

therefore

$$\rho = \frac{j\rho_0}{(\omega - \gamma u_0)} \nabla \cdot \bar{v}$$

$$\rho = \frac{j\rho_0}{\omega_b} \nabla \cdot \bar{v} \qquad \text{A3.16}$$

APPENDIX 4

Analysis of the Brillouin Flow Case
(Rigrod and Lewis [25])

The equations of motion required are:

$$\ddot{r} - r\dot{\theta}^2 = -\eta[E_{rt} + B_{zt}r\dot{\theta}] \qquad \text{A4.1}$$

$$\frac{1}{r}\frac{d}{dt}(r^2\dot{\theta}) = -\eta[-B_{zt}\dot{r} + B_{rt}\dot{z}] \qquad \text{A4.2}$$

$$\ddot{z} = -\eta[E_{zt} - B_{rt}r\dot{\theta}]. \qquad \text{A4.3}$$

For an axially symmetric field we obtain from Busch's theorem,

$$\dot{\theta}_0 = \omega_L - \frac{\eta B_c r_c^2}{2r^2}, \quad \text{where} \quad \omega_L = \frac{\eta B_{z0}}{2}.$$

If at the cathode $\dot{\theta}_1 = 0$, Eqn A4.1 becomes

$$\ddot{r}_1 = -\eta E_r + r\left(\omega_L - \eta\frac{B_c r_c^2}{2r^2}\right)^2 - \eta B_{z0} r\left(\omega_L - \eta\frac{B_c r_c^2}{2r^2}\right). \qquad \text{A4.4}$$

In Brillouin flow, $B_c = 0$ and $B_{z0} = B_B$,

therefore $\qquad\qquad \ddot{r}_1 = -\eta E_r + r\omega_L^2 - \eta B_B r\omega_L$

where $\omega_L = \eta(B_B/2)$ now.

For a cylindrical beam $\ddot{r}$ must be zero,

therefore $\qquad\qquad \eta E_r = -r\omega_L^2,$ $\qquad\qquad$ A4.5

therefore $\qquad\qquad \eta\frac{\partial V}{\partial r} = r\omega_L^2.$ $\qquad\qquad$ A4.5a

or $\qquad\qquad\qquad V = V_a + \frac{r^2\omega_L^2}{2\eta},$

where $V_a \equiv$ potential on the axis.

Equating potential and kinetic energies we get,

$$(\dot{z})^2 + (r\dot{\theta})^2 = 2\eta V$$

$$= 2\eta \left(V_a + \frac{r^2 \omega_L^2}{2\eta} \right)$$

therefore $\dot{z} = u_0 = \sqrt{(2\eta V_a)}.$

Now if the initial position of an electron was (r_0, θ_0, z_0) at time t, its co-ordinates are

$$[r_0, (\theta_0 + \omega_L t), (z_0 + u_0 t)].$$

When perturbed, the co-ordinates become

$$r = r_0 + r_1(r_0) e^{j[\omega t - \gamma(z_0 + u_0 t)]}$$

$$\theta = \theta_0 + \omega_L t + \theta_1(r_0) e^{j[\omega t - \gamma(z_0 + u_0 t)]}$$

$$z = z_0 + u_0 t + z_1(r_0) e^{j[\omega t - \gamma(z_0 + u_0 t)]}$$

$[r, \theta, z$ are functions of the radial co-ordinate $r_0]$.

The equations A4.1, A4.2 and A4.3 for the perturbed beam, are

$$\ddot{r}_1 - (r_0 + r_1)(\omega_L + \dot{\theta}_1)^2 = -\eta \left[-\frac{\partial V_0}{\partial r} + E_r + (r_0 + r_1)(\omega_L + \dot{\theta}_1)B_B \right] \quad \text{A4.6}$$

$$(r_0 + r_1)\ddot{\theta}_1 + 2\dot{r}_1(\omega_L + \dot{\theta}_1) = \eta \dot{r}_1 B_B. \qquad \text{A4.7}$$

$$\ddot{z} = -\eta E_z. \qquad \text{A4.8}$$

Eqn A4.5a becomes

$$\eta \frac{\partial V_0}{\partial r} = (r_0 + r_1)\omega_L^2.$$

Eqn A4.7 gives $\dot{\theta}_1 = 0.$

Eqn A4.8 gives $z_1 = \dfrac{\eta E_z}{(\omega - \gamma_0)^2}.$ A4.9

Eqn A4.6 gives

$$\ddot{r}_1 - (r_0 + r_1)\omega_{\mathrm{L}}^2 = \eta\,\frac{\partial V_0}{\partial r} - \eta E_r - \eta(r_0 + r_1)\frac{\omega_{\mathrm{L}}^2 2}{\eta},$$

$$\therefore\ \ddot{r}_1 - (r_0 + r_1)\omega_{\mathrm{L}}^2 = (r_0 + r_1)\omega_{\mathrm{L}}^2 - \eta E_r - 2(r_0 + r_1)\omega_{\mathrm{L}}^2$$

$$\therefore\ \ddot{r}_1 = -\eta E_r$$

$$\therefore\ r_1 = \frac{\eta E_r}{(\omega - \gamma u_0)^2}\,. \qquad\qquad \text{A4.10}$$

Analysis of the Arbitrary Field Case

(Brewer [32])

Eqn A4.4, on expansion and simple manipulation, becomes

$$\ddot{r}_1 = -\eta E_r + r(\Omega^2 - \omega_L^2) \qquad \text{A5.1}$$

where $\Omega = \eta(B_c r_c^2/2r^2)$.

For the unperturbed condition, assuming the rippling is small, Eqn A5.1 gives

$$-\eta \frac{\partial V_0}{\partial r} = r(\Omega^2 - \omega_L^2).$$

Substituting B_{z0} for B_B in Eqn A4.6, and manipulating, gives

$$\ddot{r}_1 + r\Omega^2 = -\eta E_r.$$

Thus the equations give

$$z_1 = \frac{\eta E_z}{(\omega - \gamma u_0)^2}.$$

$$r_1 = \frac{\eta E_r}{(\omega - \gamma u_0)^2 - 4\Omega^2}.$$

Now Eqn 3.16 is

$$\rho = \frac{j\rho_0}{\omega_b} \nabla \cdot \bar{v},$$

so we now have

$$\rho = \frac{j\rho_0}{\omega_b} \left[\frac{1}{r} \frac{\partial}{\partial r}(rv_r) + \frac{\partial v_z}{\partial z} \right] \qquad \text{A5.2}$$

and
$$v_r = j\omega_b r_1 \,,$$

$$\therefore \; v_r = j\omega_b \frac{\eta E_r}{(\omega_b^2 - 4\Omega^2)}$$

$$\therefore \; v_r = \frac{-\omega_b \eta}{\gamma(\omega_b^2 - 4\Omega^2)} \cdot \frac{\partial E_z}{\partial r} \,. \qquad \text{(from A3.7}_2\text{)}$$

Similarly

$$v_z = j\omega_b \eta \frac{E_z}{\omega_b^2} \,,$$

therefore
$$\frac{\partial v_z}{\partial z} = -j\gamma \cdot j\eta \frac{E_z}{\omega_b} = \gamma \frac{\eta}{\omega_b} E_z \,.$$

Therefore Eqn A5.2 becomes

$$\rho = \frac{j\varepsilon_0}{\gamma} \frac{\omega_p^2}{\omega_0^2} \left[\frac{1}{r} \frac{\partial}{\partial r} \left(r \frac{\partial E_z}{\partial r} \right) \right] - j\gamma \frac{\omega_p^2}{\omega_b^2} \varepsilon_0 E_z \qquad \text{A5.3}$$

where $\omega_0^2 = \omega_b^2 - 4\Omega^2$.

The convection current density components required are,

$$J_r = \rho_0 v_r$$
and
$$J_z = \rho_0 v_z + \rho u_0 \,,$$

therefore
$$J_r = \frac{-\rho_0 \omega_b \eta}{\gamma \omega_0^2} \cdot \frac{\partial E_z}{\partial r} \qquad \text{A5.4}$$

and
$$J_z = \frac{\rho_0 \gamma \eta E_z}{\omega_b} + \rho u_0 \,. \qquad \text{A5.5}$$

Substituting into the wave equation A3.8 gives, on simple manipulation,

$$\frac{1}{r} \frac{\partial}{\partial r} \left(r \frac{\partial E_z}{\partial r} \right) - \gamma^2 \left[\frac{\dfrac{\omega_p^2}{\omega_b^2} - 1}{\dfrac{\omega_p^2}{\omega_0^2} - 1} \right] \cdot E_z = 0 \,. \qquad \text{A5.6}$$

[It was assumed that $\gamma \simeq \gamma_0$].

Therefore
$$\frac{1}{r} \frac{\partial}{\partial r} \left(r \frac{\partial E_z}{\partial r} \right) - \tau_2^2 E_z = 0 \,,$$

where
$$\tau_2^2 = \gamma^2 \frac{\left[\dfrac{\omega_p^2}{\omega_p^2} - 1 \right]}{\left[\dfrac{\omega_p^2}{\omega_0^2} - 1 \right]} \,. \qquad \text{A5.7}$$

Finally,
$$G_z = \rho_0 u_0 r_1 \,,$$

therefore
$$G_z = \rho_0 u_0 \frac{\eta E_r}{\omega_0^2}$$

therefore
$$G_z = - \frac{\varepsilon_0 u_0 \omega_p^2 E_r}{\omega_0^2} \,. \qquad \text{A5.8}$$

APPENDIX 6

Higher-Order Space-Charge Waves

In solving Eqn 2.4 (p. 14)

$$-\frac{\sqrt{(-g)}J_1(\sqrt{(-g)}\tau_1 b)}{J_0(\sqrt{(-g)}\tau_1 b)} = \frac{I_1(\tau_1 b) - \dfrac{G_z}{F_z}\bigg|_1 K_1(\tau_1 b)}{I_0(\tau_1 b) + \dfrac{G_z}{F_z}\bigg|_1 K_0(\tau_1 b)}$$

for γ, Hahn found that there are an infinite number of solutions, *i.e.* an infinite number of space-charge waves propagate on the system (Fig. 3). Similarly, Ramo found that there are an infinite number of solutions to Eqn 2.14 (p. 20)

$$-(Tb)\frac{J_1(Tb)}{J_0(Tb)} = (\tau b)\frac{I_1(\tau b) - D'K_1(\tau b)}{I_0(\tau b) + D'K_0(\tau b)}.$$

The solutions to this equation were given by

$$\frac{T^2}{(\gamma^2 - k^2)} = \left\{ \frac{\omega_p^2}{(\omega - \gamma u_0)^2} - 1 \right\} \qquad \text{(from Eqn 2.15)}$$

assuming $\gamma \simeq \gamma_0$ and $\gamma^2 \gg k^2$ and

$$\gamma = \frac{\omega}{u_0}(1 \pm \delta_1) \qquad \text{(Eqn 2.16)}$$

where $\delta_1 = \left\{ \dfrac{\omega_p^2}{\omega^2 + T^2 u_0^2} \right\}^{\frac{1}{2}}$.

Note that the solutions paired [Eqn 2.16] and that each of these last three equations applies to each pair of solutions – to each 'order' of space-charge waves. Similarly the theory given in Chapter 2 applies to each order.

Ramo pursued the question of the higher order modes of propagation a little further and derived the equation

$$-(T_n b) \frac{J_1(T_n b)}{J_0(T_n b)} \simeq (\gamma_0 b) \frac{\left[K_0(\gamma_0 a) I_1(\gamma_0 b) - I_0(\gamma_0 a) K_1(\gamma_0 b)\right]}{\left[K_1(\gamma_0 a) I_0(\gamma_0 b) - I_1(\gamma_0 a) K_0(\gamma_0 b)\right]} = S$$

n is the number of order of space-charge wave. This equation is solved graphically as in the simpler analysis.

A far more detailed investigation was carried out by Cullen and Stephenson [a]. They were primarily concerned with experiments on a klystron, but also considered theoretically the amplitudes of the various orders of waves. They found that the amplitude of the nth order waves was proportional to

$$\frac{1}{\delta_{1n}} \left\{ \frac{1}{(T_n b) \left[1 + \frac{(T_n b)^2}{S^2} \right]} \right\}.$$

If both n and T_n are large, the amplitude of the nth order waves is proportional to T_n^{-3}. The current output at various drift lengths, for the first four orders, was calculated and the results reproduced below.

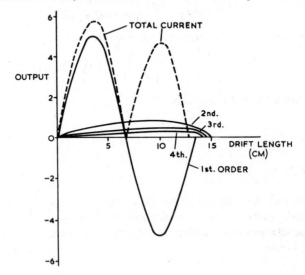

(These curves were calculated using dimensions and parameters used in their experimental apparatus:

$$V_0 = 150 \text{ V} \quad I_0 = 20 \text{ mA} \quad b = 1 \text{ cm} \quad a = 3 \cdot 2 \text{ cm}).$$

It is clearly seen that for these particular parameters, the amplitude of the second order r.f. current standing wave is substantially less than that of the first order, and that it is lower still for the third and fourth orders. Thus, after the first few orders the higher orders can be neglected. One obvious effect of the higher-order modes is illustrated by the curve of the total current. The second maximum is less than the first, but if higher orders are ignored successive current maxima have the same magnitude. Thus the higher orders produce damping of the current standing wave. One might ask if this could account for some of Mihran's results (Section 4.4 and Figures 85 and 86).

Readers particularly interested in this subject might also read a paper by Beck [b] who studied this subject in considerable detail.

References

[a] CULLEN, A. L. and STEPHENSON, I. M. (1958), 'An experimental investigation of velocity-modulated electron beams', *Proc. I.E.E.*, **105 Pt.B,** Sup. 12, 843.

[b] BECK, A. H. W. (1957), 'Higher-order space-charge waves in klystrons', *J. Electron*, **2,** 489.

Principal Symbols and Notation

a	Radius of drift tube (Also used as parameter)
a.c.	Alternating currents
$\mathbf{A}$	Magnetic vector potential
A	A parameter (Also used as initial loss)
A'	A constant
A''	Cross-sectional area
b	Radius of electron beam
$\mathbf{B}$	Magnetic flux density vector
B_B	Brillouin field
B_c	Cathode magnetic flux density
B_S	Susceptance
B_z	z component of magnetic flux density
c	Velocity of light ($2 \cdot 99 \times 10^8$ m/second)
C	Gain parameter for the travelling-wave tube
C'	A constant
C_1	A constant (Also used as a coefficient of inductance)
C_2	A coefficient of inductance
C_m	A coefficient of inductance
d.c.	Direct current
D'	A constant
$\mathbf{D}$	Electric flux density vector (electric displacement)
$-e$	Electronic charge ($1 \cdot 602 \times 10^{-19}$ coulomb)
$\mathbf{E}$	Electric field vector
E^*	Llewllyn coefficient
E	Space-charge wave coefficient for an accelerated beam
E'	Space-charge wave coefficient for a retarded beam (Also used as a constant)

f	Frequency (Also used as a function)
$\mathbf{F}$	Force vector
F^*	Llewellyn coefficient.
F	Space-charge wave coefficient for an accelerated beam
F'	Space-charge wave coefficient for a retarded beam
g	$1 - \dfrac{\omega_p^2}{\omega_b^2}$
G	Gain per section or gain per unit length (Also used as a parameter)
G_z	z component of surface current line density
G_θ	θ component of surface current line density
$\mathbf{H}$	Magnetic field vector
H^*	Llewellyn coefficient
H	Space-charge wave coefficient for an accelerated beam
H'	Space-charge wave coefficient for a retarded beam
I^*	Llewellyn coefficient
I	Space-charge wave coefficient for an accelerated beam (Also used as total current)
I'	Space-charge wave coefficient for a retarded beam
$I_{B(tot)}$	Total body convection current
$I_{S(tot)}$	Total surface convection current
$I_{C(tot)}$	$I_{B(tot)} + I_{S(tot)}$
I_n	Modified Bessel function of the nth order, 1st kind
j	$\sqrt{-1}$
$\mathbf{J}$	Convection current density vector
J_m	'Mean' convection current density
J_n	Bessel function of the nth order, 1st kind
J_0	d.c. convection current density
$J_{0(e)}$	Effective d.c. convection current density
k	ω/c (Also used for dielectric constant)
K	$\dfrac{r_c^2 B_c}{r^2 B_{z0}}$ $\left(\text{Also used as} = u_0 z^{-1} \text{ and as } \dfrac{\gamma(u_{01} - u_{02})}{2} \cdot \dfrac{1}{\omega_p}\right)$
K_n	Modified Bessel function of the nth order, 2nd kind
l	$= \dfrac{\sqrt{\omega_{p1}\,\omega_{p2}}}{\omega m'}$

L	A parameter
m	Electronic mass $(9 \cdot 1 \times 10^{-31}$ kilogram$)$
m'	$\frac{1}{2}\left\{\sqrt{\left(\dfrac{u_{01}}{u_{02}}\right)} - \sqrt{\left(\dfrac{u_{02}}{u_{01}}\right)}\right\}$
n	Number density of electrons $\left(\text{Also used as } \sqrt{\left(\dfrac{\omega_{p1} u_{02}}{u_{01} \omega_{p2}}\right)}\right)$
p	Plasma frequency reduction factor for beams in arbitrary longitudinal magnetic fields $\left(= \dfrac{(\omega - \gamma u_0)}{\omega_p} = \dfrac{\omega_b}{\omega_p}\right)$
$\bar{p}$	Phase factor (real part of a plasma frequency reduction factor)
P	Power flow
P_c	Phase constant $(= \sqrt{(X_{\dot{R}} B_S)})$
P_e	Poynting vector
P_k	Kinetic power flow per unit area
P_{el}	Electro-magnetic power flow
q	Gain factor (imaginary part of plasma frequency reduction factor)
QC	Space-charge parameter for the travelling-wave tube
r	Radius
r_c	Radius of cathode
r_n	Power ratio
r_0	Undisturbed radial position of an electron
r.f.	Radio frequencies
R	Plasma frequency reduction factor $(= \omega_q / \omega_p)$
R_1	Ratio of drift tube to beam radius $(= a/b)$
R'	Resistance per unit length of resistive coating
t	Time
T, T_0, T_1	Parameters
$\mathbf{u}$	Velocity vector
$\bar{u}_0$	Total d.c. velocity of electrons
u_0	d.c. velocity of electrons
u_{01}, u_{02}	d.c. velocity of electrons in beams 1. and 2. respectively.
u_s	Velocity separation of electrons $\left(= \dfrac{2(u_{01} - u_{02})}{(u_{01} + u_{02})}\right)$

u_m	'Mean' velocity of electrons $\left(= \dfrac{2u_{01}u_{02}}{(u_{01}+u_{02})} \right)$
u_g	Group velocity
u_p	Phase velocity
U	A parameter
U'	A parameter
U_V	An a.c. 'voltage'
v	a.c. velocity of electrons
$\bar{v}$	Total a.c. velocity of electrons
V	a.c. potential
V_0	d.c. potential
V_m	Potential difference corresponding to 'mean' velocity u_m
W	Stored energy per unit length (Also used as $= \omega_e^2/\omega^2$)
W_e	Electro-magnetic stored energy per unit volume
W_k	Kinetic energy per unit volume
x	A parameter
X	Reciprocal of the square of the plasma frequency reduction factor p
X_R	Reactance
Y	Admittance
Y_B	Beam admittance
Y_W	Wall admittance
Y_n	Bessel function of the nth order, 2nd kind
z_0	Optimum length of drift tube
Z	Impedance
α	Attenuation constant
β	Phase constant
γ	Propagation constant $(j\gamma = \alpha + j\beta)$
γ_0	ω/u_0 (Also used as ω/u_m)
Γ	A parameter
$\delta, \delta_1, \delta_2, \delta_4$	Parameters
∇	The operator 'Del'
ε_0	Dielectric constant of free space $(= 8\cdot8485 \times 10^{-12}$ farads/m)

ε'	Relative dielectric constant
ε	$= \varepsilon_0 \varepsilon'$
η	Ratio of electronic charge to mass $(= 1 \cdot 759 \times 10^{11} \text{ coulomb/kilogram})$
λ_0	Plasma wavelength
λ_s	Wavelength of standing wave
μ_0	Permeability of free space $(4\pi \times 10^{-7} \text{ henrys/m})$
μ'	Relative permeability
μ	$= \mu_0 \mu'$
ρ	a.c. charge density
ρ_0	d.c. charge density
ρ_m	Charge density of a medium
ρ_s	Charge density of beam (when used in conjunction with ρ_m)
ρ_t	Total charge density $(= \rho_0 + \rho)$
σ	Conductivity
τ_0	A parameter (Also used as d.c. transit time)
$\tau, \tau_1, \tau_2, \tau_3$	Parameters
ϕ	Magnetic flux
ϕ_c	Magnetic flux linking the cathode $(= \pi r_c^2 B_c)$
ω	Angular frequency of perturbations (signal)
ω_b	Doppler shifted frequency $(\omega - \gamma u_0)$
ω_c	Cyclotron frequency $\left(= \dfrac{eB_{z0}}{m} \right)$
ω_L	Lamor frequency $\left(= \dfrac{eB_{z0}}{2m} \right)$
ω_0^2	$= \omega_b^2 - 4\Omega^2$
ω_p	Natural frequency of plasma oscillations $\left(= \sqrt{\left(\dfrac{-\eta \rho_0}{\varepsilon_0} \right)} = \sqrt{\left(\dfrac{ne^2}{m\varepsilon_0} \right)} \right)$
ω_q	Effective plasma frequency
Ω	$= \dfrac{\eta \phi_c}{2r^2 \pi}$

Note: The suffix 0 indicates the d.c. part of any quantity, for example,

E_0 is the d.c. part of the electric field, and we use $E_t = E_0 + E$ where E is the a.c. part of the electric field. Similarly $\rho_t = \rho_0 + \rho$ etc., but note that $u = u_0 + v$. The suffices x, y, z, r, and θ indicate those components of the quantity concerned.

The un-perturbed radial position of an electron is (r_0, θ_0, z_0) and the perturbed radial position is $(r_0 + r_1), (\theta_0 + \theta_1), (z_0 + z_1)$.

Unless otherwise stated rationalized M.K.S. units are used throughout.

References

Chapter 1

[1] CLAVIER, A. G. (1933), 'Production and utilization of micro-rays', *Elect. Commun.*, **12,** 3.

[2] HEIL, A. and HEIL, O. (1935), 'A method for the production of short, undamped electromagnetic waves of great intensity', *Z. Phys.*, **95,** 752.

[3] HANSEN, W. W. (1938), 'A type of electrical resonator', *J. appl. Phys.*, **9,** 654.

[4] VARIAN, R. H. and VARIAN, S. F. (1939), 'A high frequency amplifier and oscillator', *J. appl. Phys.*, **10,** 140.

[5] HAHN, W. C. and METCALF, G. F. (1939), 'Velocity-modulated tubes', *Proc. I.R.E.*, **27,** 106.

[6] WEBSTER, D. L. (1939), 'Cathode-ray bunching', *J. appl. Phys.*, **10,** 501.

[7] HAHN, W. C. (1939), 'Small-signal theory of velocity-modulated electron beams', *Gen. Elect. Rev.*, **42,** 258.

[8] KOMPFNER, R. (1947), 'Travelling-wave tube as amplifier of microwaves', *Proc. I.R.E.*, **35,** 124.

[9] PIERCE, J. R. (1947), 'Theory of the beam type travelling-wave tube', *Proc. I.R.E.*, **35,** 111.

[10] TONKS, L. and LANGMUIR, I. (1929), 'Oscillations in ionized gases', *Phys. Rev.*, **33,** 195.

[11] HUTTER, R. G. E. (1960), *Beam and wave electronics in microwave tubes*, Van Nostrand.

Chapter 2

[12] RAMO, S. (1939), 'Space-charge and field waves in an electron beam', *Phys. Rev.*, **56,** 276.

[13] RAMO, S. (1939), 'The electronic-wave theory of velocity-modulation tubes', *Proc. I.R.E.*, **27,** 757.

[14] HAHN, W. C. (1939), 'Wave energy and transconductance of velocity-modulated electron beams', *Gen. Elect. Rev.*, **42,** 497.

[15] PIERCE, J. R. (November 1954), 'The wave picture of microwave tubes', *Bell Syst. Tech. J.*, **33,** No. 6, 1343.

[16] PARZEN, P. (1952), 'Space-charge wave propagation in a cylindrical electron beam of finite lateral extensions', *J. appl. Phys.*, **23,** 215.

REFERENCES 213

[17] WATKINS, D. A. (1952), 'Travelling-wave tube noise figures', *Proc. I.R.E.*, **40** (I), 65.

[18] SULLIVAN, J. W. (1954), 'A wide-band voltage-tuneable oscillator', *Proc. I.R.E.*, **42** (II), 1658.

[19] JAHNKE, E. and EMDE, F. (1948), *Tables of Higher Functions*.

[20] BRANCH, G. M. and MIHRAN, T. G. (1955), 'Plasma frequency reduction factors in electron beams', *I.R.E. Trans.*, **Ed. 2.** No. 2, 3.

[21] BRANCH, G. M. (1955), 'Reduction of plasma frequency in electron beams by helices and drift-tubes', *Proc. I.R.E.*, **43,** (II), 1018.

[22] BIRDSALL, C. K. and SCHUMACHER, F. M. (1959), 'Plasma frequency reduction in electron stream by helices and drift-tubes', *I.R.E. Trans.*, **Ed-6,** No. 4, 468.

[23] BIRDSALL, C. K. and BREWER, G. R. (1954), 'Travelling-wave tube characteristics for finite values of *C*', *I.R.E. Trans.*, **Ed-1,** No. 3, 1.

[24] HARMAN, W. W. (1953), *The fundamentals of electronic motion*. McGraw Hill.

[25] RIGROD, W. W. and LEWIS, J. A. (March 1954), 'Wave propagation along a magnetically focussed cylindrical electron beam', *Bell Syst. Tech. J.*, **33**, No. 2, 399.

[26] ZWORYKIN, V. K., MORTON, G. A., RAMBERG, E. G., HILLIER, J. and VANCE, A. W. (1945), *Electron optics and the electron microscope*, John Wiley & Sons.

[27] FEENBERG, E. and FELDMAN, D. (1946), 'Theory of small-signal bunching in a parallel electron beam of rectangular cross-section', *J. appl. Phys.*, **17**, 1025.

[28] LABUS, J. (1957), 'Space-charge waves along magnetically focused electron beams', *Proc. I.R.E.*, **45**, 854.

[29] LABUS, J. and PÖSCHL, K. (1955), 'Space-charge waves on ion-free electron beams', *A.Ë.U.*, **9**, 39.

[30] RIGROD, W. W. and LABUS, J. (1958), 'Space-charge waves along magnetically focused electron beams', *Proc. I.R.E.*, **46**, 358.

[31] BECK, A. H. W. (1958), *Space-charge waves and slow electro-magnetic waves*. Pergamon Press.

[32] BREWER, G. R. (1956), 'Some effects of magnetic field strength on space-charge wave propagation', *Proc. I.R.E.*, **44**, 896.

[33] NEWTON, R. H. C. (1957), 'On space-charge waves,' *J. Electron*, **2**, 441.

[34] NEWTON, R. H. C. (1958), 'Magnetic oscillations in electron beams', *Proc. I.E.E.*, **105B** (Sup. 12), 642.

[35] NEWTON, R. H. C. (1958), 'On space-charge waves', *J. Elec. & Contr.*, **5**, 510.

[36] TREVENA, D. H. (1959), 'On space-charge waves', *J. Elec. & Contr.*, **6**, 50.

[37] NEWTON, R. H. C. (1959), Comments on a paper by D. H. Trevena entitled 'On space-charge waves', *J. Elec. & Contr.*, **6**, 321.

[38] PASCHKE, F. (1959), 'The propagation of perturbations along magnetically focused electron beams', *R.C.A. Rev.*, **20**, 254.

[39] KENT, G. (1962), 'Perturbation of electron flow', *J. appl. Phys.*, **33**, 683.

[40] PIERCE. J. R. (1950), *Travelling-wave tubes*, Van Nostrand.

[41] CUTLER, C. C. and QUATE, C. F. (1950), 'Experimental verification of space-charge and transit-time reduction of noise in electron beams', *Phys. Rev.*, **80**, 875.

[42] BERGHAMMER, J. (1954), *Die Welligkeit eines magnetisch geführten Elektronenstrahles*, Dip. Ing. Thesis, Technische Hochschule Vienna.

[43] SCHNITGER, H. (1953), 'Die Messung der Welligheit des Elektronenstrahles einer Wanderfeldröhre', *A.Ё.U.*, **7**, 415.

[44] LAWSON, J. D. (1955), 'Some experiments on a cylindrical electron beam constrained by a magnetic field', *J. Electron*, **1**, 43.

[45] SCHUMANN, W. O. (1956), 'Über Wellenausbreitung im Plasma zwischen zwei unendlich gut leitenden Ebenen in Richtung eines aufgeprägte äusseren Magnetfeldes', *Z. angew. Phys.*, **8**, 482.

Chapter 3

[46] FIELD, L. M., TIEN, P. K. and WATKINS, D. A. (1951), 'Amplification by acceleration and deceleration of a single-velocity stream', *Proc. I.R.E.*, **39**, 194.

[47] TIEN, P. K. and FIELD, L. M. (1952), 'Space-charge waves in an accelerated electron stream for amplification of microwave signals', *Proc. I.R.E.*, **40**, 688.

[48] LLEWELLYN, F. B. and PETERSON, L. C. (1944), 'Vacuum tube networks', *Proc. I.R.E.*, **32**, 144.

[49] BIRDSALL, C. K. (1956), 'Equivalence of Llewellyn and space-charge wave equations', *I.R.E., Trans.*, **Ed. 3**, No. 2, 76.

[50] PETER, R. W. (1952), 'Low noise travelling-wave amplifier', *R.C.A. Rev.*, **13**, 344.

[51] SMULLIN, L. D. (1951), 'Propagation of disturbances in one-dimensional accelerated electron streams', *J. appl. Phys.*, **22**, 1496.

[52] BIRDSALL, C. K. (1954), 'Rippled-wall and rippled-stream amplifiers', *Proc. I.R.E.*, **42**, 1628.

[53] BLOOM, S. and PETER, R. W. (1954), 'Transmission-line analog of a modulated electron beam', *R.C.A. Rev.*, **15**, 95.

[54] CHU, L. J. (1951), *Paper to I.R.E. conference on electron tubes*, Durham, N.H., U.S.A.

[55] PETER, R. W., BLOOM, S. and RUETZ, J. A. (1954), 'Space-charge wave amplification along an electron beam by periodic change of the beam impedance', *R.C.A. Rev.*, **15**, 113.

[56] BIRDSALL, C. K. and WHINNERY, J. R. (1953), 'Waves in an electron stream with general admittance walls', *J. appl. Phys.*, **24**, 314.

[57] MIHRAN, T. G. (1954), 'Scalloped-beam amplification', *J. appl. Phys.*, **25,** 1341.

[58] BLOOM, S. (1954), *'Space-charge waves in a drifting, scalloped beam'*, R.C.A. Internal Technical Report.

[59] MIHRAN, T. G. (1956), 'Scalloped-beam amplification', *I.R.E. Trans.*, **Ed. 3,** No. 1, 32.

[60] PIERCE, J. R. (July 1951), 'Waves in electron streams and circuits', *Bell Syst. Tech. J.*, **30,** No. 3, 626.

[61] CHU, L. J. and JACKSON, J. D. (1948), 'Field theory of travelling-wave tubes', *Proc. I.R.E.*, **36,** 853.

[62] BIRDSALL, C. K., BREWER, G. R. and HAEFF, A. V. (1953), 'The resistive-wall amplifier', *Proc. I.R.E.*, **41,** 865.

[63] CHU, L. J., *A.C. kinetic energy in electron streams*, Private communication.

[64] WALKER, L. R. *The Easitron* and *some Easitron amplifier structures*, Internal Memoranda.

[65] KOMPFNER, R. (1952), 'Travelling-wave tubes', *Rep. Progr. Phys.*, **15,** 275.

[66] MUELLER, W. M. (1961), 'Propagation in periodic electron beams', *J. appl. Phys.*, **32,** 1349.

[67] PIERCE, J. R. (1948), 'Possible fluctuations in electron streams due to ions', *J. appl. Phys.*, **19,** 231.

[68] PIERCE, J. R. (1949), 'Increasing space-charge waves', *J. appl. Phys.*, **20,** 1060.

[69] PIERCE, J. R. and HEBENSTREIT, W. B. (Jan. 1949), 'A new type of high-frequency amplifier', *Bell. Syst. Tech. J.*, **28,** No. 1, 33.

[70] HOLLENBERG, A. V. (Jan. 1949), 'Experimental observation of amplification by interaction between two electron streams', *Bell. Syst. Tech. J.*, **28,** No. 1, 52.

[71] PIERCE, J. R. (1949), 'Double-stream amplifiers', *Proc. I.R.E.*, **37,** 980

[72] HAEFF, A. V. (1948), 'Space-charge-wave amplification effects', *Phys. Rev.*, **74,** 1532.

[73] HAEFF, A. V. (1949), 'The electron wave tube – A novel method of generation and amplification of microwave energy', *Proc. I.R.E.*, **37,** 4.

[74] NERGAARD, L. S. (1948), 'Analysis of a simple model of a two-beam growing wave tube', *R.C.A. Rev.*, **9,** 585.

[75] BEAM, W. R. (1955), 'On the possibility of amplification in space-charge potential-depressed electron streams', *Proc. I.R.E.*, **43,** (I), 454.

[76] LOPUKHIN, V. M. and ROSHAL, A. S. (1962), 'Beating wave amplifier operating with opposed electron streams', *Radiot. i. Eleck*, **7,** 604.

[77] VURAL, B. (1961), 'Analysis of double-stream interaction in the presence of a finite axial magnetic field', *R.C.A. Rev.*, **22,** 753.

[78] FEINSTEIN, J. and SEN, H. K. (1951), 'Radio wave generation by multi-stream charge interaction', *Phys. Rev.*, **83,** 405.

[79] YADAVALLI, S. V. (1961), 'The penetration of an electron beam through a plasma', *J. Elec. & Contr.*, **10**, 437.

[80] PIDDINGTON, J. H. (1956), 'Growing electric space-charge waves and Haeff's electron wave tube', *Phys. Rev.*, **101**, 14.

[81] PIDDINGTON, J. H. (1956), 'Growing electric space-charge waves', *Aust. J. Phys.*, **9**, 31.

[82] PIDDINGTON, J. H. (1958), 'Growth of electric space-charge and radio waves in moving ion streams', *Phil. Mag.*, **3**, 1241.

[83] STURROCK, P. A. 'Kinematics of growing waves', *Phys. Rev.*, **112**, 1488.

[84] PIERCE, J. R. and WALKER, L. R. (1956), 'Growing electric space-charge waves', *Phys. Rev.*, **104**, 306.

[85] SWIFT-HOOK, D. T. (1960), 'Validity of the theory of double-stream amplification', *Phys. Rev.*, **118**, 1.

[86] BUNEMAN, O. (1958), 'Instability, turbulence and conductivity in current-carrying plasma', *Phys. Rev. Letters*, **1**, 8.

[87] DRUMMOND, J. E. (Editor), (1961), *Plasma physics*, McGraw-Hill.

[88] DAVIES, M. C. (1961), *Electron beam parametric amplifiers*, Lond. Univ. M. Sc. Dissertation.

[89] LOUISELL, W. H. (1960), *Coupled mode and parametric electronics*, John Wiley and Sons.

[90] HAEFF, A. V. (1949), 'On the origin of solar radio noise', *Phys. Rev.*, **75**, 1546.

[91] PARZEN, P. (1951), 'Theory of space-charge waves in cylindrical wave-guides with many beams', *Elect. Commun.*, **28**, 217.

Chapter 4

[92] MACDONALD, D. K. C. (1949), 'Transit-time deterioration of space-charge reduction of shot effect', *Phil. Mag.*, **40**, 561.

[93] WATKINS, D. A. (1952), 'The effect of velocity distribution in a modulated electron stream', *J. appl. Phys.*, **23**, 568.

[94] RACK, A. J. (Oct. 1938), 'Effect of space-charge and transit time on the shot noise in diodes', *Bell Syst. Tech. J.*, **17**, No. 4, 592.

[95] GOLDSTEIN, H. (1950), *Classical Mechanics*. Addison Wesley.

[96] LINDSAY, R. B. (1951), *Physical Mechanics*. Van Nostrand.

[97] KENT, G. (1954), 'Space-charge waves in inhomogeneous electron beams', *J. appl. Phys.*, **25**, 32.

[98] YADAVALLI, S. V. (1954), 'On some effects of velocity distribution in electron streams', *Quart. appl. Maths.*, **12**, 105.

[99] DAY, W. D. (1960), *Introduction to Laplace transforms*. Iliffe and Sons.

[100] WATKINS, D. A. and RYNN, N. (1954), 'The effect of velocity distribution on travelling-wave tube gain', *J. appl. Phys.*, **25**, 1375.

[101] GRAY, G. A. (1960), 'Single-velocity equivalents for multi-velocity electron streams', *J. appl. Phys.*, **31**, 370.

[102] CARROL, J. E. (1963), 'A single-velocity analysis of a multi-velocity electron stream', *J. Elec. & Contr.*, **14**, 403.

[103] GRAY, F. (Oct. 1951), 'Electron streams in a diode', *Bell Syst. Tech. J.*, **30**, No. 4, Pt. I, 830.

[104] SIEGMAN, A. E. (1960), *Signal propagation on a drifting electron beam with a square velocity distribution*, Internal Memoranda.

[105] SIEGMAN, A. E. (1957), 'Analysis of multi-velocity electron beams by the density-function method', *J. appl. Phys.*, **28**, 1132.

[106] BERGHAMMER, J. (1962), 'Landau damping of space-charge waves', *J. appl. Phys.*, **33**, 1499.

[107] MIHRAN, T. G. (1962), 'R.F. current behaviour in electron beams with d.c. velocity spread', *J. appl. Phys.*, **33**, 1582.

[108] BLOOM, S. and VURAL, B. (1963), 'Space-charge wave decay along a signal-current-excited multi-velocity beam', *J. appl. Phys.*, **34**, 2007.

[109] SIEGMAN, A. E., WATKINS, D. A. and HSUNG-CHENG HSIEH, (1957), 'Density-function calculations of noise propagation on an accelerated multi-velocity electron beam', *J. appl. Phys.*, **28**, 1138.

[110] SMULLIN, L. D. and HAUS, H. A. (1959), *Noise in electron beams*, M.I.T. Press.

[111] CAULTON, M., HERSHENOV, B. and PASCHKE, F. (1962), 'Experimental evidence of Landau damping in electron beams', *J. appl. Phys.*, **33**, 800.

Chapter 5

[112] WALKER, L. R. (1954), 'Stored energy and power flow in electron beams', *J. appl. Phys.*, **25**, 615.

[113] LOUISELL, W. H. and PIERCE, J. R. (1955), 'Power flow in electron beam devices', *Proc. I.R.E.*, **43**, (I), 425.

[114] SLATER, J. C. (1950), *Microwave electronics*, Van Nostrand.

[115] WALKER, L. R. (1955), 'Power flow in electron beams', *J. appl. Phys.*, **26**, 1031.

[116] HAUS, H. A. and BOBROF, D. L. (1957), 'Small-signal power theorem for electron beams', *J. appl. Phys.*, **28**, 694.

[117] BOBROF, D. L., HAUS, H. A. and KLUVER, J. W. (1962), 'On the small-signal power theorem of electron beams', *J. appl. Phys.*, **33**, 2932.

[118] CHU, E. L. (1959), 'Two alternative definitions of small-signals r.f. power of electron beams', *J. appl. Phys.*, **30**, 1617.

[119] KLUVER, J. W. (1962), 'Potential form of the small-signal power theorem', *J. appl. Phys.*, **33**, 2943.

[120] BEAM, W. R. (1960), 'Determination of sign of power flow in electron beam waves', *Proc. I.R.E.*, **48** (I), 1170.

[121] STURROCK, P. A. (1960), 'In what sense do slow wave carry negative energy'? *J. appl. Phys.*, **31**, 2052.

[122] HAUS, H. A. and ROBINSON, F. N. H. (1955), 'The minimum noise figure of microwave beam amplifiers', *Proc. I.R.E.*, **43**, (II), 981.

Index